HEAVEN

My Dream of What Heaven Might Be Like

*A True Story That Offers Great Comfort
for Those Who Have Loved Ones in Heaven
and Inspiration for All*

Rebecca Ruter Springer
Revision by Jann Bach

HEAVEN

My Dream of What Heaven Might Be Like

*A True Story That Offers Great Comfort
for Those Who Have Loved Ones in Heaven
and Inspiration for All*

**Rebecca Ruter Springer
Revision by Jann Bach**

AYLEN
PUBLISHING

P.O. Box 1999
Mt. Dora, Florida 32756

© 2007 by Bobb Biehl
Printed in the United States of America
0-9765040-7-3
Published by Aylen Publishing
P.O. Box 1999
Mt. Dora, FL 32756
Subject Heading: Leadership / Personal Growh
ISBN 0-9765040-7-3

DEDICATION

Lovingly dedicated in memory of:

Jenny Leigh Bach
March 26, 1976 – February 29, 1984

Evida Alberta Biehl
March 19, 1924 – November 26, 2003

Joseph Henry Kimbel
May 12, 1913 – March 27, 2005

TABLE OF CONTENTS

Proven Tools to Help in Adjusting to New Life Realities

Heaven

Biography

Authors's Biography

This book was originally published by the David C. Cook Publishing Company in 1898 under the title, *Intra Muros*. It was written by Rebecca Ruter Springer.

Rebecca was born in Indianapolis, Indiana on November 8th, 1832, the daughter of Rev. Calvin Ruter, a Methodist Episcopal clergyman. In 1850, Rebecca graduated from the Wesleyan Female College in Cincinnati, Ohio and on December 15, 1859 she married William McKendree Springer. Rebecca and William had a son named Ruter, and the family resided in Washington, D.C., where Rebecca's husband was a prominent congressman. Rebecca died in 1904, shortly after the death of her husband.

Editors's Biography

Jann Bach was employed as a Family Support Coordinator/ Clinical Outpatient Therapist for nearly twenty years. She currently works for Masterplanning Group, Int'l. as a Special Projects Coordinator. Jann resides in Northern Michigan with her husband, Jerry, where they are actively involved in the prayer ministry at Pathway Community Church.

Intra Muros was a source of great comfort to my family and me when we lost beloved family members. I found myself wishing, though, that an updated, more contemporary version were available, so families with young children could easily read it together as they worked through their grief. This version – called *Heaven* - is the result of that wish.* I have tried to update the material without sacrificing the "old-world" charm of the original work. My prayer is that you and your loved ones will feel the comfort of His presence and blessing, as you read the words of this little book.

* This was possible, since there is no copyright on the edition from which this material was taken.

INTRODUCTION

The pages of this little book contain no fancy story, written to entertain. Rather, this is the true record of an experience during days when life hung in the balance between Time and Eternity – with the scales dipping decidedly toward the eternal side.

I am painfully aware of the fact that I can never adequately paint for others, the scenes as they appeared to me during those wonderful days. However, if I can only dimly show the close connection between our earthly and heavenly lives, I may be able to help others understand that death need not be something to fear; it can instead be an open door into a new and beautiful phase of the lives we now live.

If any of the scenes depicted should seem to be irreverent, please realize that they were clearly not intended to be so. I have tried to describe everything as it came to me: the close blending of our earthly and heavenly lives, the glad surprises, and the divine joys – intensified and illumined by the reverence, love, and adoration given to the blessed Trinity.

With the hope that this narrative may comfort and uplift you, as these memories will ever do for me; I submit this imperfect sketch of a most perfect vision.

Chapter 1

I was hundreds of miles away from home and friends, and had been very ill for many weeks. I was entirely among strangers. My only attendant, though very kind, knew nothing about caring for someone who was ill. Therefore, I had none of the delicate care that keeps an invalid's strength from failing. I had taken very little nourishment, including water, and was greatly reduced in both size and strength.

Consciousness seemed at times to wholly desert me. I had an indescribable longing for the presence of my dear, distant ones - for the gentle touch of beloved hands, and whispered words of love and encouragement. However, they never came – they could not. Responsible duties that I felt must not be neglected, kept these dear ones in distant places, and I would not ask them to come.

I lay in a large, comfortable room on the second floor of a house in Kentville. The bed was placed in a little nook at one end of the apartment. From this nook, a large stained glass window opened upon a terrace, which faced the street. During much of my illness, I lay with my face toward this window and my back to the room. I remember wishing that I could somehow pass through the window to the terrace.

When the longing for the loved, distant faces and voices became more than I felt I could bear, I prayed that the Lord would help me to feel His blessed presence; and that since the beloved ones of earth could not minister to me, I might feel the influence of the dear ones who were in heaven. I asked especially to be sustained, should I be called to face death alone. It was no idle prayer, and the response came swiftly.

All anxieties and cares slipped away from me, like the darkness at sunrise; and peace, Christ's peace, enfolded me. I was willing to wait until God's perfect time for the coming of those so dear to me. I often said to myself, "If not here, in heaven – there is no fear of disappointment there."

During those days of agonized suffering, yet great peace, I felt that I had truly found the refuge of the "Everlasting Arms." They lifted me; they enfolded me; and I rested in them, as a tired child would rest upon its mother's bosom.

One dark and stormy morning, after a day and night of intense suffering, I seemed to be standing by the bed. When I looked up, I saw my husband's favorite brother (who had died many years ago) standing beside me.

"My dear brother Robert," I cried out joyously, "how good of you to come!"

"It was a great joy to me that I could do so, little sister," he said tenderly. "Shall we go now?" he asked, as he drew me toward the window.

I turned my head and looked back into the room, which somehow I felt I was about to leave forever. It was in its usual good order - a cheery, pretty room. The attendant sat by the stove at the farther end. She appeared to be comfortable and was reading a newspaper.

On the bed - turned toward the window - lay a still, white form. I noticed the shadow of a smile on the poor, worn face. My brother drew me gently, and I yielded. We passed through the window, out to the terrace, and from there – in some unaccountable way – down to the street. There, I paused and said earnestly, "I cannot leave Will and our dear boy."

"They are not here, dear, but hundreds of miles away," he answered.

"Yes, I know, but they will be here. Oh, Robert, they will need me – let me stay," I pleaded.

"Would it not be better if I brought you back a little later – after they come?" he said, with a kind smile.

"Would you surely do so?" I asked.

"Most certainly, if you desire it. You are worn out with the long suffering, and a little rest will give you new strength."

I felt that he was right, said so in a few words, and walked slowly with him along the street. He had drawn my hand through his arm and tried to interest me in conversation. My heart, though, clung to the dear ones whom I felt I was not to see again on earth. Several times I stopped and looked wistfully back toward the way from which we had come.

He was very patient and gentle with me, always waiting until I was ready to proceed again. At last my hesitation became so great that he said pleasantly, "You are so weak, I think I should carry you." Without waiting for a reply, he stooped and lifted me in his arms, as though I were a child – and, like a child – I yielded, resting my head upon his shoulder. Placing my arm around his neck, I felt so safe and content to be in his care. It seemed very sweet after the long, lonely struggle, to have someone assume the responsibility of caring so tenderly for me.

He walked on with firm, swift steps – and I think I must have slept – for the next thing I knew, I was lying in a little sheltered area. Flowering shrubs that grew upon the softest, most beautiful turf of grass I had ever seen, formed the shelter. It was thickly studded with fragrant flowers, including many I had known and loved on earth. I remember noticing the heliotrope, violets, lilies of the valley, and mignonette, along with many other flowers that were unfamiliar to me.

In that first moment, I observed the perfection of every plant and flower. For instance the heliotrope, which on earth often grows into long, ragged sprays – there, grew upon short, smooth stems. Each leaf was perfect, smooth, and glossy, instead of being rough and coarse-looking. The flowers peeped up, from the deep velvet-like grass, with sweet, happy faces, as though inviting the admiration one could not withhold.

What a scene unfolded before my eyes, as I rested upon this soft, fragrant cushion – secluded, and yet not hidden. I somehow knew this perfect expanse of grass, trees, and flowers extended far beyond the limit of my vision.

The wonderful trees had drooping branches, which were laden with exquisite blossoms and fruits of many kinds. I found myself thinking of St. John's vision on the Isle of Patmos - and the "tree of life" that grew beside the river, bearing "twelve manner of fruits", and whose leaves were for the "healing of the nations."(Revelation; KJV)

Beneath the trees, in many happy groups, were little children – laughing and playing, running in their joy! They caught, in their tiny hands, the bright-winged birds and butterflies that flitted in and out among them, joyfully sharing in their play.

All through the grounds, people were leisurely walking – sometimes in groups, sometimes by twos, sometimes alone – with an air of peacefulness and happiness that could be felt, even though I was a stranger. All were clothed in spotless white, though many wore or carried clusters of beautiful flowers.

In every direction, I saw - half-hidden by the trees - elegant and beautiful houses of unusual, attractive architecture. I thought these must be the homes of the happy inhabitants of this enchanted place.

I caught glimpses of numerous sparkling fountains and a peaceful, flowing river -with water as clear as crystal. The pathways that extended in many directions were pure and spotless pearl. They were bordered by narrow streams of pristine water, which trickled over stones of gold.

The one thought that repeatedly came to mind as I looked upon this scene was, "purity, purity." No shadow of dust; no hint of decay on fruit or flower; everything perfect, everything pure. The grass and flowers looked as though summer showers had freshly washed them. Not a single blade of grass was any color but the brightest green. The air was soft and balmy, though invigorating. Instead of sunlight, there was a golden and rosy glory everywhere - somewhat like the afterglow of a Southern sunset in midsummer.

As I drew in my breath with a short, quick gasp of delight, I heard Robert say softly, "Well?" Looking up, I discovered that he was watching me with heartfelt enjoyment. I had, in my great surprise and delight, wholly forgotten his presence. An overpowering sense of God's goodness swept over me, and I dropped my face into my hands.

"Ah," said my brother, in a tone of self-reproach. "I am inconsiderate." Lifting me gently to my feet, he said, "Come, I want to show you the river."

When we reached the bank of the river, I found that the lovely foliage continued to the water's edge. As I looked down, I saw that the flowers also bloomed tranquilly in the depths, among the many-colored pebbles with which the entire bed of the river was lined.

"I want you to see and feel these beautiful, smooth stones," said my brother, as he stepped into the water and urged me to do the same. I drew back timidly, saying, "I fear it is cold."

"Not in the least," he said, with a reassuring smile. "Come."

"Just as I am?" I asked, as I glanced down at my lovely robe that, to my great joy, I found was similar to those of the others in that happy place.

"Just as you are," he added, with another reassuring smile.

I stepped into the gently flowing river. To my great surprise, I found the water in both temperature and density almost identical with the air. The stream became deeper and deeper as we walked on, until I felt the soft, sweet ripples playing around my throat. As I stopped, my brother said, "A little farther still."

"It will go over my head," I exclaimed.

"Well, and what then?"

"I cannot breathe under the water – I will suffocate." An amused twinkle came into his eyes, though he said seriously enough, "We do not do those things here."

I realized the absurdity of my comment and with a happy laugh said, "All right, come on." I plunged headlong into the bright water, which soon bubbled and rippled several feet above my head. To my delight, I found I could breathe, laugh, talk, see, and hear as naturally under the water as I could above it. I sat down in the midst of the many-colored pebbles and filled my hands with them, as a child would have done. My brother lay down upon them and laughed and talked joyously with me.

"Do this," he said, as he rubbed his hands over his face and ran his fingers through his dark hair.

I did as he told me, and the sensation was delightful. I threw back my loose sleeves and rubbed my arms, then my throat. I again thrust my fingers through my long hair and thought about how tangled it would be when I left the water.

When at last we arose to return to the bank of the river, I wondered what we were to do for towels. Some of the "earth-thoughts" still clung to me and, as we approached the shore, I assumed that my lovely robe had been ruined. As we emerged from the water, however, I realized that I would need no towel or brush. My skin, hair, and even my beautiful clothes were as soft and dry as they had been before the water touched them.

The design of my robe and the material from which it was made, were unlike anything I had ever seen. The material was soft, light, and shimmered with a faint luster. It reminded me of silk crepe more than anything else I could recall, but was infinitely more beautiful. It fell around me in soft, graceful folds. The water – amazingly - seemed to cause the fabric to become even more lustrous than it was before.

"What marvelous water! What wonderful air!" I said to my brother, as we again stepped upon the flowery expanse. "Are all of the rivers here like this one?"

"Not just the same, but similar," he replied.

We walked a few more steps before I turned and looked back at the shining river, flowing so gently. "Robert, what has that water done for me? I feel as though I could fly."

He looked at me with earnest, tender eyes as he answered gently, "Each time you enter the river, it washes away remnants of the 'earth-life' and prepares you for the new life upon which you have entered."

"It is divine!" I whispered."

"Yes," he said, "it is divine."

Chapter 2

We walked in silence for some distance, my heart delighting in this new, wonderful life - my eyes drinking in fresh beauty with every step. The houses, as we approached and passed them, seemed wondrously beautiful to me.

They were built of the finest marble and were encircled by broad terraces. Massive pillars or delicate columns supported the roofs. Winding steps led down to the pearl walkways. The style of architecture was unlike anything I had ever seen.

Flowers and vines, that grew luxuriantly, surpassed in beauty those of my brightest dreams. Happy faces looked out from these celestial homes, as cheerful voices of children playing on the lawns rang upon the clear air.

"Robert, where are we going?" I asked.

"Home, little sister," he answered tenderly.

"Home – have we a home, my brother? Is it anything like these?" I asked. A wild desire was rising in my heart to cry out for joy.

"Come and see," was his only answer. He turned onto a side path, which led toward an exquisitely beautiful house. Its columns of very light gray marble, shone through the green of the overhanging trees with inviting beauty. Before I could join him, I heard a well-remembered voice close beside me:

"I just had to be the first to welcome you!" Turning around, I saw the dearly beloved face of my long-time friend, Mrs. Harris.

"Oh! Oh!" I cried, as we met in a warm embrace.

"You will forgive me, Colonel Stratton," she said a moment later, giving her hand cordially to my brother. "It seems unforgivable to interrupt you this way so soon, but I heard that she was coming, and I could not wait. Now that I have looked upon her face and heard her dear voice, I will be patient until I can have her for a long, long talk."

"You must come in and see her now," said my brother graciously.

"Do, do come!" I urged.

"No, dear friends, not now. You know, dear little Blossom"(a nickname I had many years ago), "we have all of eternity before us – but you will bring her to me soon, Colonel Stratton?" she asked.

"Just as soon as I may, dear lady," he replied, looking expressively into her eyes.

"Yes, I understand," she said softly, with a compassionate glance toward me. Then, with a warm handclasp and the parting request, "Come very soon," she passed swiftly out of my sight.

"Blessed woman," I said. "What a joy to meet her again!"

"You will often see her. She is indeed a lovely woman. Now, come, little sister. I want to welcome you to our home."

He took my hand and led me up the low steps to a broad terrace. It had a beautiful inlaid floor of rare and costly marble and massive columns of gray. (Broad terraces surrounded both levels of the entire house.)

Hanging between the beautiful, marble columns were luxurious vines. They were covered with rich, glossy leaves of green and flowers of exquisite color and delicate perfume. We paused here for a moment, so I could see the charming view presented on every side.

"It is heavenly!" I said.

"It is heavenly," he answered. "It could not be otherwise."

I smiled my acknowledgment of this truth – my heart was too full for words.

He led me through a doorway that was between two marble columns. After entering a large, impressive reception hall with massive windows, we walked across the inlaid floor toward a broad, low stairway.

Before I could speak, my brother turned to me. Taking both of my hands into his, he said: "Welcome, a thousand welcomes, dearest sister, to your heavenly home."

"Is this beautiful place truly to be my home?" I asked, as well as my emotions would allow.

"Yes, dear," he replied. "I built it for you and my brother, and I assure you it has been a labor of love."

"It is your home, and I am to stay with you?" I said, a little confused.

"No, it is your home, and I am to stay with you until my brother comes."

"Always, dear brother, always!" I cried, clinging to his arm.

He smiled and said, "We will enjoy the present; we will never be far apart again. Come, I am eager to show you everything."

Turning to the left, he led me through beautiful marble columns that seemed to be substituted for doorways. As we entered a large, oblong room, I stopped in wondering delight. The marble walls and floor of the room were polished to the greatest luster; but over walls and floor were strewn exquisite, long-stemmed roses. There was every variety and color, from the deepest crimson to the most delicate shades of pink and yellow.

"Come inside," said my brother.

"I do not wish to crush those perfect flowers," I answered.

With a twinkle in his eye, he asked, "Shall we gather some of them?"

I bent down to take one from the floor close to my feet, but found that it was imbedded in the marble. I tried another with the same astonishing result. Turning to my brother, I said: "What does it mean? Is it possible that none of these are natural flowers?"

With a pleased smile, he answered: "This room has a history. Come in and sit with me upon this window-seat. I want you to see the whole room, as I tell you about it." I did as he desired, and he continued. "One day as I was busily working on the house, a group of young people came to the door. They asked if they could enter. I gladly gave permission, and then one of them said:

" 'Is this house really for Mr. And Mrs. Stratton?'

" 'It is,' I answered.

" 'We know and love them. They are our friends, and the friends of our parents. May we do something to help you make it beautiful?'

" 'Indeed you may,' I said, touched by the request. 'What do you have in mind?'

"We were in this very spot at the time. As one of the girls looked around, she asked, 'May we beautify this room?'

" 'Certainly,' I said, wondering what they would try to do.

"At once the girls, all of whom had immense bunches of roses in their hands, began to throw the flowers over the floor and against the walls. Wherever the flowers struck the walls - to my surprise – they remained, as though they were permanently attached. When the freshly gathered roses had all been scattered, the room looked just as it does now.

"Then, the boys each produced a small case of delicate tools. In a moment, all of the boys and girls were down upon the marble floor and busy at work. How they did it I do not know – it is one of the celestial arts, taught to those with highly artistic tastes. They embedded each living flower just as it had fallen in the marble, and preserved it as you see before you. They came several times before the work was completed, for the flowers here do not wither or fade, but are always fresh and perfect.

"What a merry, happy group of young people! They laughed, chatted, and sang as they worked. I could not help but wish that the friends who mourn for them could look in upon this happy group, and see how little cause there is for sorrow.

"When they were finished, they asked me to come and see what they had done. I was hearty with my praise, both for the beauty of the work and for their skill in performing it. Then, saying they would be sure to return when either of you came, they went away together – no doubt to do something of the kind elsewhere."

Happy tears had been dropping upon my hands, which were clasped in my lap, during much of this narrative. I asked half-brokenly, for I was greatly touched: "Who are these lovely people, Robert? Do you know them?"

" I know them now, but with the exception of Molly Stratton, they were all strangers to me until they came here that first morning."

"Who are the others?"

"There were three named Mary – Mary Green, Mary Bates, Mary Chalmers - also Mae Camden. These were the girls, each lovely and beautiful. The boys - all fine young men - were Mark Ashland, Matthew Chalmers, and David Chalmers."

"Precious children!" I said. "Little did I know that my love for them, in the olden days, would bring to me this added happiness! How little we know of the links binding the two worlds."

"Ah, Yes!" said my brother, "that is just it. How little we know. If only we could realize while we are yet on earth, that day-by-day we are building for eternity, how different our lives would be. Every gentle word, every generous thought, every unselfish deed, will become a pillar of eternal beauty in the life to come. We cannot be selfish and unloving in one life, and generous and loving in the next; the two lives are too closely blended, one but a continuation of the other."

Rising, we crossed the room that from this time on was to hold for me such tender associations, and entered the library. My immediate sensation upon entering the room was genuine surprise at the sight of the books. My first words were: "We have books in heaven?"

"Why not?" asked my brother.

What strange ideas we humans sometimes have, of the pleasures and duties of heaven. We seem to think that death of the body means an entire change to the soul. That is not the case, however. We bring to our new lives many of the same tastes, desires, and knowledge we had before. How unfortunate it would be if all that we experienced on earth were lost when we die.

The more we learn during our probationary time on earth, the more competent we will be to carry our understanding forward to completion and perfection in heaven. The purer the thoughts, the nobler the ambitions, the loftier the aspirations – the higher the rank we take among the heavenly hosts.

"Who writes the books – are any of the authors those we knew and loved below?"

"Yes, many of them; especially those who helped to elevate the human mind or immortal soul. Many of the extraordinary minds in the earth-life, upon entering this higher life, gain elevated and extended views of their lifelong studies. Pursuing them with passion, they write out the deeper views they have acquired.

"These individuals remain leaders and teachers in this extraordinary place, as they were while yet in the world. Is it to be expected that the great authors, who have uplifted so many lives while on earth, should lay their writing aside when their clear brains and pure hearts have read the mysteries of the higher knowledge? Never! After they learn their lessons well, they write them out for the benefit of others.

"Leaders there must always be – in this divine place, as well as on earth – leaders and teachers in many varied lines of thought. The gifts that we used on earth are not lost; rather, they are perfected and become increasingly *more* useful to us and to those with whom we share this glorious life."

Chapter 3

The library was a glorious room. Its walls were lined, from ceiling to floor, with magnificent, luxuriously bound books. A large, stained-glass window opened upon the front terrace. Two large bow windows, not far apart, were in the back of the room.

A semicircular row of shelves, which was supported by very delicate pillars of gray marble, extended some fifteen feet into the spacious room. These shelves cut the room into two sections – lengthwise – each, with one of the bow windows in the back. This left a large space beyond the dividing line, where the two sections united again into one.

The concave side of the semicircle of shelves was toward the entrance of the room. A beautiful writing desk, completely furnished for use, stood near one of the bow windows. Upon the desk, a bowl of pure gold was filled with scarlet carnations. They exuded a spicy odor of which I had been faintly aware for some time.

"My brother's desk," said Robert.

"And his favorite flowers," I added.

"In this place, we never forget the tastes and preferences of those we love."

It is not to be supposed that I at once noticed these details; rather, they were unfolded to me gradually as we lingered, talking together.

After a short rest in this lovely room among the books, my brother took me through the remaining rooms of the house. The entire second story was finished with inlaid woods of fine, satiny texture and rare polish. Each room was perfect and beautiful in its own, unique way. There was so much perfection in every detail; it took many visits before I could fully appreciate the beauty of these rooms, which are now eternally photographed upon my memory.

I will speak of only one of these rooms at this time. As Robert led me upstairs to the columned doorway of a lovely room, he opened the filmy gray draperies – which were lined with the most delicate shade of amber - and said: "Your own 'special place' for rest and study."

The room we now entered was exquisite in design and finish. It was rectangular in shape, with a large bow window at one end – similar to those in the library, a portion of which was directly beneath this room. Within this window – on one side – stood a writing desk of solid ivory with silver trim. Opposite the desk, was a matching ivory bookcase with well-filled shelves, in which I was later to find books by many of my favorite authors.

Magnificent rugs, silver-gray in color, were scattered over the floor. All of the draperies in the room were of the same delicate hue and texture as those at the entrance.

The framework of the furniture was ivory. The chairs, pillows, and sofa were covered with the finest silver-gray satin.

A large bowl of finely crafted silver was filled with beautiful roses and placed upon a table, near one of the windows. There were also several elegant vases of flowers, which filled the air with a lovely fragrance. The entire room was beautiful beyond description.

Only one picture hung upon the walls, and that was a life-size portrait of the Christ, just opposite the sofa. It was not an artist's conception of the human Christ, bowed under the weight of the sins of the world – nor was it the thorn-crowned head of the crucified Savior of mankind. It was the likeness of the living Master; of Christ the victorious; of Christ the King. The wonderful eyes looked directly and tenderly into my own, and the lips seemed to pronounce a benediction of peace. I do not have the capacity to describe the beauty of the divine face, which seemed to illuminate the room with a holy light.

I fell upon my knees as my heart cried, "Master, beloved Master and Savior!" It was a long time before I could focus my attention on anything else; my whole being was filled with adoration and thanksgiving for the great love that had guided me into this haven of rest, this wonderful home of peace and joy.

After spending a considerable amount of time in this delightful room, we stepped through the French doors, onto the marble terrace. A stairway of artistically sculpted marble wound gracefully down to the lawn beneath the trees. No pathway of any kind approached the bottom of the stairway – only the flowery turf.

The fruit-laden branches of the trees hung within easy reach of the terrace. I noticed seven varieties as I stood there that morning. One kind resembled our fine Bartlett pear, but was much larger. I also soon discovered that they were infinitely more delicious.

Another variety was in clusters. This fruit, also pear-shaped, was smaller than the former. Its consistency and flavor was similar to the finest ice cream. A third, something like a banana in shape, was called breadfruit. It was not unlike our dainty pastries to the taste.

It seemed to me at the time - and later proved to be so – that, in variety and excellence, food for the most elegant meal was provided without labor or care. My brother gathered some of the different varieties of food and asked me to try them. I did so with much pleasure and refreshment. One time, the rich juice from the pear-like fruit ran abundantly over my hands and the front of my dress. "Oh!" I cried. "I'm afraid I have ruined my clothes!"

My brother laughed kindly, as he said, "Show me the stains."

To my amazement, I could not find a single stain.

"Look at your hands," he said.

I found them to be clean and fresh, as though I had just bathed. "How can this be? My hands were covered with the thick juice of the fruit."

"No impurity can remain for an instant in this air. Nothing decays, nothing tarnishes – or in any way disfigures or mars – the universal purity or beauty of this place. As fast as the fruit ripens and falls - all that is not immediately gathered - evaporates, with not even the seed remaining." Ah, yes, this was the reason there was no fruit on the ground.

We descended the steps and again entered the "flower room." As I stood admiring the inlaid roses, my brother asked: "Whom, of all the loved ones you have in heaven, do you most wish to see?"

Without hesitation I answered, "My father and mother."

He smiled so significantly that I quickly turned. Walking toward me, I saw my dear father, mother, and my youngest sister. They appeared to me exactly as they had the last time I saw them in the earth-life, except that they were refined and purified – perfect in every way. With a cry of joy, I flew into my father's outstretched arms. I heard his dear, familiar voice saying, "My precious, little daughter!"

"At last!" I cried, clinging to him. "At last I have you again!"

"At last!" he echoed, with a deep-drawn breath of joy. Then, we turned to my dear mother and were soon locked in an embrace.

"My precious mother!" "My dear, dear child!" we cried simultaneously. My sister, enfolding both of us in her arms, exclaimed with a happy laugh, "I cannot wait! I will not be left outside!" Disengaging one arm, I threw it around her and pulled her closer – into the happy circle of our united love.

Oh, what an hour that was! I did not dream that even heaven could hold such joy. After a time my brother, who had been rejoicing with us, said: "I have other work to do, so I will leave you for a while to continue this blessed reunion."

"Yes," said my father, "we understand that you must go. We will – with joy – continue to watch over our dear child."

"Then, for a brief while, goodbye," my brother said gently. "Do not forget that rest, especially to one who has so recently entered upon the new life, is one of the pleasures of heaven."

"Yes," said my father, with a kind smile and peaceful expression. "We will see that she does not forget."

From that point forward, my daily interaction with the dear ones in heaven from whom I had so long been separated, served to restore the feeling of "being home" that had been the greatest comfort of my human life. I began to realize that *this* was indeed the *true* life, instead of the probationary life that I had always regarded with such importance.

Chapter 4

As time passed, and I grew more accustomed to the heavenly life around me, I found its loveliness unfolding like the gradual opening of a rare flower. Delightful surprises met me at every turn: A dear friend, who had gone to heaven many years ago, would come unexpectedly to me with a warm greeting; one that I admired greatly on earth, but from whom I had remained distant – fearing I would be an unwelcome intrusion – would lovingly approach me; the clear revelation of some truth, only partly understood in life – though eagerly pursued – would become clear, overwhelming me with the realization of the close tie that links the earth-life with the divine.

One of the most wonderful surprises was the occasional meeting with someone I had never thought would make it to heaven. With eager handclasp and tearful eyes, they would express sincere thanks for some helpful words or actions that had been instrumental in turning their hearts toward God. Oh, the joy to me of such a revelation; but also, the wish that my earth-life had been more full of such work for eternity.

My first daily impulse upon awakening from happy, blissful rest was to hurry to the "river of life" and plunge into its wonderful waters. They were so refreshing, invigorating, and inspiring - my heart filled with thanksgiving and my lips overflowed with joyful praise. I sometimes went with my brother, at other times went alone. I always returned to our home filled with new life, hope, and purpose.

One morning, as I was on my way to the river, my voice joined in with the wonderful song of praise that seemed to be everywhere. As I was singing, I saw a lovely young girl walking briskly toward me with outstretched arms.

"Dear, dear Aunt Sara!" she called, as she drew near.

"My little Mae!" I cried, gathering her into my arms. "Let me look at you, dear." I held her a moment at arm's length, then drew her tenderly to me. "You have grown very beautiful, my child. You were always lovely; you are simply radiant now. Is it this divine life?"

"Yes," she said modestly and sweetly, "but most of all it's because I am near the Savior so much."

"Ah, yes, that is it – being near Him would make any being more radiant and beautiful," I said.

"He is so good to me – so generous, so tender. He seems to forget how little I have done to deserve His care."

"He knows you love Him, dear heart; that means everything to Him."

"I love Him a thousand times more than anything on earth or in heaven." The sweet face grew increasingly more radiant and beautiful as she talked about the Master. I began to vaguely understand the wonderful power of Christ among those who are in heaven.

During her brief life, this dear child was exceptionally lovely and good – as we define goodness on earth: yet, she had seemed to be too absorbed in having fun to truly focus on the things she treasured in her heart. In this heavenly life, she counted the privilege of loving Christ, of being near Him, beyond every other joy! Just as a great earthly love shines through an individual's face, so this divine love lifts and glorifies the one who loves until not only the face, but also the entire person radiates the glory that fills the heart.

"Come with me to the river, Mae," I said, after we had talked together for some time. "Come with me for a delightful swim."

"Gladly," she said, "but have you ever been to the lake or the sea?"

"The lake or the sea?" I echoed. "No, I haven't. I didn't know there was a lake or a sea."

"Well, you do now," said Mae delightedly. "Shall we go to the lake today and leave the sea for another day? Which shall it be?"

"Let it be the lake today," I said.

Turning in an entirely different direction from the path that led to the river, we walked on, still talking as we went. There was so much to ask, recall, and look forward to with joy!

At one point, she turned to me and asked excitedly: "When is my Uncle Will coming?"

I affectionately patted her hand and said, "That is in God's hands; His timing is always perfect."

"Yes, I know. His will is always right, but I long to see my dear uncle again; and to 'long' is not to complain."

This child of tender years had become so womanly and wise. It was a joy to talk with her. I told her how much I longed to be with the dear ones I left behind.

"Yes, yes, I know it all," she whispered. She placed her soft arms around me and said, "but it will not be long. They will come soon. It never seems as though it's a long wait for anything here. There is always much to keep us busy; many pleasant duties and joys – oh, it will not be long!"

She continued to cheer and comfort me as we walked through the ever varying and always perfect landscape. Eventually we arrived at the lake, and as we did so she cried, "Look – is it not divinely beautiful?"

I caught my breath, then stopped abruptly and covered my face with my hands to shield my eyes from the glorified scene. No wonder my brother had not previously brought me to this place; I was barely strong enough spiritually – at this time – to look upon it. When I again slowly lifted my head, Mae was standing like one who was entranced. The golden morning light rested upon her face, and mingling with the radiance that came from within, almost transfigured her. Even Mae, who had long been an inhabitant here, had not yet grown accustomed to its glory.

"Look, darling auntie. It is God's will that you should see," she whispered softly, not once turning her eyes away from the scene before her. "I'm so glad He is allowing me to be the one to show you the glory of this place!"

I turned and looked, like one only half awakened. Before us, spread a lake that was as smooth as glass. It was flooded with a golden glory, caught from the heavens, which made it like a sea of molten gold.

The blossoming and fruit-bearing trees grew down to its very border in many places. A great number of people were resting upon the lake's flowery bank.

Far, far away, across its shining waters, arose the domes and spires of what seemed to be a mighty city. The city and its reflection in the lake, was more beautiful than anything I could have imagined.

On the surface of the water, were graceful boats of wonderful design. They were filled with happy souls and propelled by an unseen force. Little children, as well as grown persons, were floating upon or swimming in the water. As we looked upon this scene, a choir of cherubs – floating high overhead – drifted across the lake. Their baby voices sang to us in notes of joyful praise.

"Come," said Mae, seizing my hand.

"Glory and honor," sang the child voices. "Dominion and power," answered the voices of the vast crowd. Mae and I spontaneously joined in the singing. The cherub choir floated onward. In the distance, we caught the faint melody of their sweet voices and the response from those waiting below.

We stood upon the border of the lake. My cheeks were covered with tears, and my eyes became misty with emotion. I felt as weak as a little child, but oh, what rapture – what joy unspeakable - filled and overwhelmed me!

Mae slipped her arm around me and whispered, "Come, dear auntie. After the ecstasy – rest!"

I surrendered without objecting; I could not do otherwise. She led me into the water – down, down into its crystal depths. When it seemed to me we must be hundreds of feet beneath the surface, she threw herself face downward and encouraged me to do the same. I did so and immediately began to rise.

I soon found that we were no longer rising, but were slowly floating in mid-current, many feet beneath the surface. Then, a wonderful thing appeared to me: everywhere I looked, perfect prismatic rays surrounded us. We seemed to be resting in the heart of a prism. Such vivid – yet delicate – coloring, human eyes have never seen. These colors blended in such rare graduation of shades as to make the rays seem infinite – or they really were so; I could not decide which was true.

As I was watching this marvelous panorama (for the colors deepened and faded like the lights of the aurora borealis), the sound of distant music attracted my attention. Although Mae and I no longer clung together, we did not drift apart – as one would naturally suppose we would. Although we were lying within easy speaking-distance of each other, few words were spoken by either of us. The silence seemed too sacred to be lightly broken. We rested upon – or rather within – the water, as one would rest upon the softest sofa. It required no effort whatsoever to remain afloat; the gentle movement of the water soothed and brought rest to us.

When distant music again captured my attention, I turned and looked at Mae. She smiled back at me, but did not speak. I soon comprehended the words, "Glory and honor, dominion and power" and knew it was still the cherub choir. I realized they must now be many miles away from us. Then, I heard the soft, beautiful tones of a bell. As the last notes faded away, I whispered: "Please tell me about the lake, Mae."

"Yes, dear auntie, I will tell all that I know. The waters of this lake catch the light in a most marvelous manner, as you have seen; a wiser mind than mine must tell you how this is possible. They also transmit musical sounds over a great distance."

"And what about the bell?"

"That is the silver bell – in the city across the lake, which calls people to certain tasks at this hour."

"There never was a sweeter call to duty," I said.

"Yes, its notes are beautiful. Listen: now it is playing chimes."

We lay still and enjoyed the heavenly music. As we listened, a sweet tranquility wrapped around me, and I slept as peacefully as a child in its mother's arms. I awoke with a profound sense of refreshment and strength. It was a feeling totally unlike that experienced during a bath in the river, yet I could not define the difference. Mae explained: "One takes away the last of the earth-life, and prepares us for the life upon which we are entering; the other fills us to overflowing with a drink from the Celestial Life."

I was to find that, as the days passed, I would often desire to go to the sacred lake. I would sometimes go alone, sometimes with one or more of my family members – my revered father and precious mother, my dear brother and sister – or with one of my many beloved friends. I never would grow sufficiently familiar with it to overcome the first great awe with which it inspired me. I was to find, though, that the more often I bathed, floated, or slept in its crystal-clear current, the stronger I became in spirit; and the more able I was to comprehend the mysteries of the world around me.

When we emerged from the water, we found that there were fewer people on the bank of the lake. Many had gone, at the call of the bell, to the happy assignments of the hour. Groups of children continued to play in joyous freedom. Some of them climbed trees, which overhung the water, with the agility of squirrels. They dropped with happy shouts of laughter into the lake, floating around upon its surface like beautiful water lilies or lotus flowers.

No fear of harm or danger, no dread of evil, no anxiety for fear that a disaster could occur; the faces of these children reflected security – security, joy, and peace! "This is indeed the blessed life," I commented, as we stood watching the games of the happy children.

As we turned to go Mae said, "I often think about how we were taught to believe that heaven was a place where we would wear crowns of gold and stand with harps in our hands. We do see the crowns, and we do hear the angelic harps – when and as God wills it – but the crowns of gold we usually see are the halos His blessed presence casts around us, and we do not need harps to accentuate our songs of praise; our best worship is to do His blessed will."

"You are wise in the knowledge of heaven, my child," I answered. "How happy I am to learn from one so dear. Tell me all about your life here."

As we walked, she told me the history of her years in heaven. She spoke of her duties, joys, friends, and home. I found that her home was quite a distance from my own – far beyond the spires of the great city across the lake. Mae reminded me, though, that distance is insignificant in heaven. We can come and go as we wish. We feel no fatigue or haste, experience no delays; it is blessed, truly blessed!

Not far from my home, we saw a group of children. In their midst, was a large, beautiful dog, over which they were rolling and tumbling with the greatest of freedom. As we approached, he broke away from them and came running to meet us. He affectionately crouched and played at my feet, wagging his tail excitedly.

"Do you not know him, auntie?" Mae asked.

"Why, it is dear old Sport!" I cried. I stooped down and placed my arms around his neck, resting my head on his silken hair. "Dear old fellow, how happy I am to have you here!" He responded to my caresses with obvious delight, and Mae laughed aloud at our mutual joy.

"I have often wondered if I would find him here. He surely deserves to be happy for his faithfulness and devotion in the other life. His loyalty surpassed that of many human beings."

"Didn't he sacrifice his life for little Will?"

"Yes, he attempted to cross the track in front of an approaching train. He saw that it would pass between him and his little master, and was afraid Will was in danger. He always placed himself between us and anything he thought might be threatening, but he seemed to be especially protective of Will. He was so courageous – he deserves immortality. Dear, dear old Sport, you shall never leave me again!" I said, stroking his soft coat tenderly.

At this, he sprang to his feet barking fervently and pranced before us the rest of the way home. When we arrived, he lay down upon the doorstep with an upward glance and a wag of his bushy tail, as though to say, "See how I know what you say to be true?"

"He understands every word we say," said Mae.

"Of course he does; he only lacks speech to make him perfect. I hoped he might somehow find it here."

"He has his bath in the river every day, and it leaves its mark on him, also. He lacks nothing in this life that he needs to be all that God created him to be, for his pleasure – and ours. He would not be half as interesting if he could talk," said Mae.

"Perhaps not," I reflected, trying to transition my thinking to this new way of understanding.

It occurred to me that one of the sweetest proofs we have of the Father's loving care for us, is that we so often find in this life the things that gave us great happiness below. The more unexpected this is, the greater the joy that it brings.

Mae told me the story of a beautiful little girl as she entered heaven. She was the first to come from a large and affectionate family. I learned that the despairing cry of her mother had been, "Oh, if only we had someone there to meet her, to care for her."

The little girl had arrived, lovingly nestled in the Master's arms. A while later, as He sat cuddling and talking to her, a perfect little Angora kitten came running across the grass. It sprang into her arms, where it lay contentedly. The child had been very fond of this kitten when it had become ill and – to her great sorrow – died. The little girl cried with delight as she recognized her favorite little pet. The hugs and kisses that kitten received were reported to bring happy tears to the eyes of all who witnessed the event.

Who but our loving Father would have thought of such a comfort for this child? She had apparently always been a shy little girl, but as she looked into the tender eyes above her, she began to tell Him all about her precious kitten. Jesus didn't leave her until she was playing happily among the flowers with the little friends who had gathered around her. Our Father never forgets us, but provides pleasures and comforts for us, according to our individual needs.

My longing heart began to cry out from its depths, "When shall I be able to see the Savior? When shall I meet, face to face, the *One* I love so much?"

Mae, as though understanding this silent cry, placed both arms around my neck. She looked tenderly into my eyes and whispered: "You, too, dear auntie, will see Him soon. He never delays when the time is ready for His coming. It will not be long."

Chapter 5

The following morning, after an interesting time of instruction, my brother said to me, "Shall we go for the visit we promised Mrs. Harris?"

"Oh, yes!" I answered enthusiastically. We left immediately for the much-anticipated visit.

We soon reached her lovely home and found her waiting at the entrance, as though she had been expecting us. After a courteous greeting to our friend, my brother said: "I will leave the two of you together to have that 'long talk' for which I know you are both eager, and will go to my other duties." Turning to me he said, "I will see you later at home."

"All right," I answered. "I am familiar with the way now and need no assistance."

After he had gone, my friend took me through her lovely home. She excitedly showed me the rooms that had been prepared for each beloved member of her earthly household.

One room, which she had especially designed for her cherished husband, was large and had open windows at each end. Just outside the windows – within easy reach – were trees that were heavily laden with luscious fruit and fragrant flowers. She whispered to me, "Douglas always liked a spacious room. I am sure he will like this one." I wholeheartedly agreed with her.

Returning down the broad stairway, we entered a very large music room. On three sides, it had extensive galleries that were supported by marble columns. In these galleries, were many musical instruments – harps, violins, and some unlike any instruments I had ever seen. The room itself was filled with easy chairs, sofas, and window-seats where listeners could sit while taking pleasure in the sweet harmonies.

"Our daughter," my friend explained, "who left us in early childhood, has received fine musical training here. Much to our delight, she and her young friends frequently enjoy performing for us. You know our hometown of Springville has furnished some very talented musicians and vocalists: Mary Allis, Will Griggs, and many others that I hope you will often hear in this room."

We re-entered the dainty reception hall, which opened upon the front terrace and outer steps. Mrs. Harris drew me to a seat beside her and said: "Now, tell me everything about our dear home and all of its blessed residents." We held each other's hands for hours, as we talked. Eventually, she arose with a satisfied smile and said: "I will leave you for a little while. You must not go, there is still more to come; wait here."

I had already learned not to question the judgment of these wiser friends and agreed to her request. As she passed through the doorway to the inner house, I saw a stranger at the front entrance and rose to meet him. He was tall and commanding in form, with a face of indescribable sweetness and beauty. Where had I seen him before? Surely, surely I had met him since I had come. "Ah, now I know," I thought; "it must be St. John, the beloved disciple." He had been pointed out to me, from a distance, one morning as I stood by the river.

"Peace be unto this house," was his greeting as he entered.

How his voice stirred and thrilled me! No wonder the Master loved him, with that voice and that face.

"Enter, you are a welcome guest. I will call Mrs. Harris," I said, as I approached to make him welcome.

"No, do not call her. She knows that I am here. Sit beside me for awhile." He led me to a seat and, like a child, I did as I was requested to do; still watching, always watching, the wonderful face in front of me.

"You have come recently," he said.

"Yes, I have only been here for a short while; so short that I don't know how to figure time as you do here," I answered.

"Ah, that matters little," he said with a serene smile. "Many cling always to the old way of calculating and to the earth-language. They find it is a pleasant link between the two lives. How does the change impress you? How do you find life here?"

"If those left on earth could only know! I never fully understood the meaning of that glorious scripture in Corinthians: 'No eye has seen, no ear has heard, and no mind has imagined what God has prepared for those who love Him.' It is indeed beyond human understanding." I spoke with deep feeling.

"For those who love Him? Do you believe that all Christians truly love Him?" he asked. "Do you think they love the Father for the gift of the Son – and the Son because of the Father's love and mercy; or is their worship often that of duty rather than love?" He spoke reflectively and gently.

"Oh," I said, "you know the beloved Master well and are so loved by Him, how can you doubt the love He must inspire in all hearts who seek to know Him?"

A radiant glow began to spread across the wonderful face, as he lifted his head and looked directly at me– and I *knew* Him! With a low cry of joy and adoration, I threw myself at His feet, bathing them with happy tears. He gently stroked my bowed head for a moment, and then rising, lifted me to His side.

"My Savior – my King!" I whispered, clinging closely to Him.

"Yes, and Older Brother and Friend," he added tenderly. He wiped away the tears, which were spilling from beneath my closed eyelids.

"Yes, yes, the Ruler among ten thousand, and the perfect, Holy One!" I again whispered.

"You are now beginning to encounter the circumstances of the new life. As it has been with many others, the changing from faith to sight has caused you to experience a little shyness – a little hesitancy. That is typical, although it is unnecessary. Have you forgotten the promise, 'I go to prepare a place for you, that where I am, there ye may be also?' If you loved Me when you could not see Me, love Me even more, now that we have really become 'co-heirs of the Father.' Come to Me with all that brings confusion or delight; come to your Older Brother, who is always waiting to receive you with joy."

Then, he asked me to have a seat. He talked seriously with me for a long time, unfolding many of the mysteries of the divine life. I was captivated by His words; I took pleasure in every tone of His voice. I eagerly watched every line of the beloved face and was exalted – uplifted, beyond the power of words to express.

As He concluded, He arose with a smile. "We will often meet," He said. I leaned over and pressed my lips reverently to the hand, which still clasped my own. Then, laying benevolent hands in blessing upon my bowed head, He passed noiselessly and rapidly from the house.

As I stood, watching the Savior's fast-retreating figure pass beneath the flower- laden trees, I saw two beautiful young girls approach Him. With arms linked together, they came – happily talking to each other – sweet Mary Bates and Mae Camden. When they saw the Master, they ran happily to meet Him. As He joyously extended a hand to each, they accompanied Him on His way. They looked up trustingly into His face as He talked with them, and they apparently talked freely with Him.

I saw His face – from time to time – in profile, as He turned and looked down lovingly. He looked first upon one, then the other lovely, upturned face. I thought, "That is the way He would have us be with Him – truly as children with a beloved older brother."

I was overcome with awe-inspiring emotion as I turned and walked slowly through the house, toward the beautiful rear entrance. Just before I reached the door, I met my friend Mrs. Harris. As soon as she saw me, she said: "I know all about it. Do not try to speak; I know your heart is full. I will see you very soon – go!" She kindly took my hand and led me to the door. How my heart blessed her! It indeed seemed like a sacrilege to try to talk about ordinary topics after this holy experience.

I did not follow the path, but walked across the flowery turf and beneath the trees, until I reached home. I found my brother sitting upon the terrace. As I climbed the steps, he arose to meet me. When he saw my face, he took both hands into his and very gently said, " Ah, I see. You have been with the Master!" He stepped aside, almost reverently, for me to enter the house.

I ascended the stairway to my room and dropped the draperies behind me at the door. Reclining upon the sofa with closed eyes, I relived every instant I had spent in His "Sacred Presence." I recalled every word and tone of my Savior's voice. I locked the instructions He had given me permanently upon my memory. I seemed to have been lifted to a higher plane of existence, since I had met "Him whom my soul loves."

It was a long, blessed communion that I held with my own soul on that holy day. When I looked upon the pictured face above me, I wondered why I had not immediately recognized the Christ - the likeness was so perfect. I concluded that for some wise purpose, my eyes were restrained from "seeing" until it was His pleasure that I should see Him *as He is*.

When at last I arose, the soft golden twilight enveloped me. I knelt by my sofa to offer a heartfelt prayer to the Master. As I prayed, all I could express over and over was: "I thank You, blessed Father. I thank You, I thank You!"

I later descended the stairway and found my brother standing in the great "flower-room." Going to him, I said softly: "Robert, what do we do in heaven when our hearts are overflowing with Thanksgiving?"

"We praise!" he answered.

"Then, let us praise now," I said.

With clasped hands, we lifted our hearts and voices in a hymn of praise to God; my brother led with his clear, strong voice and I followed. As the first notes sounded, I thought the roof echoed them; but I soon found that other voices blended with ours, until the whole house seemed to be filled with unseen singers. Such a majestic hymn of praise was never heard on earth.

As the hymn continued, I recognized many dear voices from the past: Will Griggs' passionate tenor, Mary Allis' exquisite soprano, and many other voices that awakened memories of long ago. I heard sweet child-voices and - looking up - saw a cloud of radiant baby-faces that flooded my heart with joy. The room seemed to be filled with them.

"Oh, what a life – what a divine life!" I whispered, as the last lingering notes faded away. My brother and I returned to the terrace and sat in the golden twilight.

"You are only in the first pages of its record," he said. "Its blessedness must be gradually unfolded to us or we could not, even here, bear its dazzling glory."

An hour of reverent conversation followed, during which he led my soul deeper into the mysteries of the glorious life I had now entered. He taught me; I listened. Sometimes I questioned, but rarely. I was content to take the "heavenly manna" as it was given to me, with a heart full of gratitude and love.

Chapter 6

The next day, my brother was working on an important mission, so I decided to look for the dear young friends I had seen briefly the day before. I knew that all things were accomplished in the correct sequence in that happy world. I knew, too, that I would find them at some point; yet, I could only hope it might be very soon. As I remembered the glowing light upon their fresh young faces when they had met the beloved Master, I longed to gather the dear girls to my heart and talk with them about their heavenly experiences.

I began to think again of my blessed interview with Him, and became so absorbed in these thoughts that I was unaware of the beautiful world around me. Suddenly, I heard someone say: "Surely that is Mrs. Stratton." Looking up, I saw sweet Mary Bates a few steps away, observing me intently.

I cried joyfully: "My precious child!" I ran to her and enfolded her in my arms. She placed her head on my shoulder in the old caressing way, almost sobbing in her great joy.

"Dear, dear Mamie." (A nickname often used by her in the past.) "How glad, how glad I am to have you here! I could hardly wait to find you."

"How did you know I was here, Mary?"

"Mae told me, and we were on our way to find you when we met the Savior, and He told us He had just left you," she said softly.

What a thrill that was to my heart! He had thought about and had spoken of me after we parted! I longed to ask her what He had said, but felt hesitant to do so. Seeming to know my thoughts, she commented: "He spoke so tenderly about you, and said we must be with you often."

"Mae had work to do today," she continued. "Since she had already seen you, I decided to come alone. She might come later, but I wanted to stay a long time with you! There is so much to tell you, so much to talk about."

"That would be delightful. I had been looking for you when we met. Come, dear child, let us go to my home at once." As we walked arm in arm I asked, "What shall we talk about first?"

"I would like to talk about my dear ones – every individual member of our beloved household. May we begin with my precious, heart-broken mother? I am with her often, but her great, unresolved sorrow keeps me from being the comfort to her I long to be. If only she could spend one hour with me here, could know God's wisdom and love as we know it, the mournful cloud would be lifted from her life. She would see that the two lives, after all, are but one."

"Yes, dear," I answered. "I always urged her to think of it in that light and to trust completely in the Father's tender care and never-failing love; but it is difficult for us to see beyond the lonely quietness and the vacant chair. Still, I believe she is beginning to feel the comfort you long for her to receive."

"She has my father and the boys – and I am still as truly hers as they are! I often sit with them, my arms around my dear, little mother – or with her hand in mine. Why is she unable to recognize my presence? This is almost complaining, though, is it not? Someday she will know everything – until then, I must be patient. We have learned to *know* that the will of the Father is always tender and wise. That is why there is no sorrow here."

We continued to talk about many of our loved ones who were still on earth. As we slowly walked on, we saw a group of four – three women and a man – standing under the trees, beside the walk. The man's back was toward us, but we immediately recognized the Master. The women were all strangers, and one of them seemed to have just arrived. The Savior held her hand as He talked with her, but all were intently listening to His words.

We greeted the group in silence as we slowly passed by. I did not expect recognition from Him at a time like this, but just as we approached them, he turned and looked at us. He did not speak – but oh, that look! His eyes were full of tenderness, encouragement, and benediction. It lifted us, enthralled, and exalted us. As we passed onward, the clasp of our hands tightened, and unspeakable rapture flooded our hearts.

We finished our walk in silence and sat down on the marble steps, beneath the overhanging trees. The dear child nestled close against my side. She laid her head upon my shoulder, while I rested my cheek caressingly upon it. After a time, I whispered partly to myself, "Was there ever such a look?"

She instantly raised her head and looking at me, said eagerly: "You think so, too? I thought you would. It is always His way. If it isn't an appropriate time to speak with you, He looks at you, and it is as though you were able to spend a long time with Him. Is He not wonderful? Why, why could we not know Him on earth as we know Him here?"

"How long were you here before you met Him?" I asked.

"Oh, that is the most wonderful part! His was the first face I looked upon after I left my earthly body. I felt confused when I first realized I was free, and I stood hesitantly for a moment. Then, I saw Him standing beside me with that same look upon His face.

"At first I felt shy, but He stretched out His hand toward me and said, ever so gently: 'My child, I have come to take care of you; trust me, do not be afraid.' In that moment, I *knew* Him, and all of my fear left instantly. I hugged Him as I would have hugged one of my brothers. He said very little to me, but somehow I felt that He knew all of my thoughts.

"I asked, 'May I stay with my mother awhile longer? Her heart is broken.'

" 'Yes, dear child, as long as you desire,' he answered compassionately.

" 'Will you stay with me?' I asked – for I already felt I could not endure having him leave me.

"He looked very pleased, as though he understood my thought. He answered, 'Yes, I will not leave you; I will wait until you are ready to go.'

"Then, I went to mother and put my arms around her. The Master came and whispered words of comfort to her, too – but I am not sure she recognized our presence.

"We stayed until everything was over. I never left her side, other than when I tiptoed into my little brother's room. He was sick and alone, so I spent a few precious minutes with him, too. I have always felt that he recognized my presence more than any of the others. He was so still and calm when I talked to him. He seemed to be listening.

"When they gathered for the last time around my casket, I felt as though I must speak, that I must show myself to them. If they could have seen me – for only an instant – standing so calmly in their midst, they would have understood that I was not in the lifeless body they had embalmed and made beautiful for burial. However, they did not recognize the truth. I pleaded with the Master to let me show myself to them, but he said, 'It is not the Father's will.' After that, I fully accepted the Father's will, and soon thereafter He brought me here in His arms. What a blessed life it is!"

"Indeed it is, Mary."

I can give only a brief outline of our conversation on that happy day, for it is too sacred to be examined by earthly eyes. We talked for many delightful hours - until the golden twilight fell - and watched the little birds nestling in the vines. From a distance, we could hear the joyous notes of the angel choir and joined our voices in the hymn of praise. We later went to my room and lay down to rest. The last words I heard before sinking into heaven's blissful sleep were tenderly whispered: "Dear, dear little Mamie, I am so glad and happy that you are here."

More than once the question has been asked, "Was there night there?" The answer is, "Emphatically, no!"

The heavenly version of our earthly day was full of a glorious radiance, a rosy golden light that was everywhere. There is no language known to humans that can describe this marvelous glory. It flooded the sky; it was caught up and reflected in the waters; it filled all heaven with joy and all hearts with song.

After a period that was much longer than our longest earthly day, this glory mellowed and softened until it became a glowing twilight full of peace. The children ceased their playing beneath the trees, the little birds settled in their nests, and all who had been busy in various ways basked in the tranquility. There was no darkness, no dusky shadows – only a restful softening of the glory.

Chapter 7

Not long after this, my brother said, "We will go to the grand auditorium this morning; it will be a rare day even here. Martin Luther will be speaking on *The Reformation; Its Causes and Effects*. This will be supplemented with a talk from John Wesley, and there may also be other speakers."

It was not the first time we had visited this great auditorium, although I have not previously described it. The ground upon which it stood was slightly elevated. Massive columns of alternating amethyst and jasper supported the mighty dome. There were no walls in the enormous building, only the great dome and supporting columns. A broad platform of precious marble rose from the center, and behind this platform hung heavy curtains of royal purple. Seats of highly polished wood ascended on three sides of the stage, forming an immense amphitheater. An altar of solid pearl stood near the center of the platform.

When we entered, we found that the building was filled with people who were eagerly waiting for what was to follow. We were soon seated and also waiting. Soft strains of melody floated around us from an invisible choir.

As the song ended, Martin Luther - in the prime of manhood - ascended the steps and stood before us. It is not my purpose to discuss his appearance, other than to say that his greater intellect and spiritual strength seemed to have increased his already powerful physique. It is impossible to outline his lecture in this brief sketch. The audience, though, was captivated by the wisdom and eloquence of his speech.

When he was finished, John Wesley took his place. The saintly beauty of his face, intensified by the heavenly light upon it, was wonderful. His theme was *God's love*; and if in the earth-life he presented it with power, he now swept our souls with the fire of his praise. He portrayed what that love had done for us, and how we could never repay God for this gift - even through an eternity of thanksgiving and worship.

Silence – except for the faint, sweet melody of the unseen choir – rested upon the vast audience for some time after he left. Everyone seemed to be deeply meditating on the theme, which had been conveyed so tenderly.

Then, the heavy curtains behind the platform parted. A tall form, around whom all the glory of heaven seemed to center, emerged from their folds and advanced toward the middle of the platform. Instantly, the vast audience arose and cried out - as with one voice - that grand anthem we had sung on earth:

> *All hail the power of Jesus' name,*
> *Let angels prostrate fall;*
> *Bring forth the royal diadem,*
> *And crown Him Lord of all.*

Such a grand chorus of voices: such unity, harmony, and volume were never heard on earth. It rose, it swelled, it seemed to fill not only the great auditorium, but also heaven itself. Above it all, we could still hear the voices of the angel choir – no longer breathing the soft, sweet melody, but bursting forth into triumphant praise. A flood of glory seemed to fill the place. Looking upward, we saw the great dome ablaze with golden light. The angelic choir was no longer invisible. With their heavenly harps and violins, their countenances reflected the radiance of the One whose praise they sang. He - before whom all heaven bowed in adoration - stood with uplifted face and kingly manner, the very God of earth and heaven. He was the center of all light. A divine radiance that was beyond comparison surrounded Him.

As the hymn of praise and adoration ceased, everyone sank slowly to their knees. Every head was bowed, and every face was covered as the angel choir exaltedly sang the familiar words:

Glory be to the Father, and to the Son, and to the Holy Ghost. As it was in the beginning, is now, and ever shall be - world without end.
   Amen, Amen!

Gradually, the voices faded away, and a holy silence fell upon us. Slowly and reverently, everyone arose and resumed their places . . .well, no, not all. Sweet Mary Bates had come with us to this sacred place. I now noticed that she was still kneeling with clasped hands and radiant, uplifted face. Her lovely eyes were focused upon the Savior with such self-forgetful adoration and love that she, too, looked truly divine. She was so intent I could not disturb her.

A moment later, the Master turned and met her adoring eyes with such a look of loving recognition, she quietly resumed her seat beside me with a deep sigh of satisfied desire. She slipped her hand into mine with the confidence of a child, who feels certain she is perfectly understood.

As I looked upon the glorious form before us, clothed in all the majesty of the Godhead, my heart tremblingly asked, "Can this be the Christ-man whom Pilate condemned to die such a horrible death upon the cross?" I could not understand it. It seemed impossible that any man, however wicked, could cause such suffering for this *One* who was so good!

Then, the Savior began to speak. The sweetness of His voice was far beyond the melody of the heavenly choir. I wish it were possible to produce His gracious words in written form, as they fell from His lips. Earth has no language through which I could convey their noble meaning.

He first talked briefly about the earth-life, and clarified so wonderfully the link of light uniting the two lives – the past with the present. He then unfolded to us some of the mysteries of the blessed life, and enthralled us with descriptions of things yet to come.

When He finished, we sat with bowed heads as He left the auditorium. Our souls were so uplifted, our spirits so exalted, our whole beings so enraptured by His divinity – that we left silently and reverently. Each of us left with the ability to see and understand more clearly - the blessed life upon which we had entered - and a heart filled with higher, more divine aspirations.

There is a depth, a mystery to all that pertains to that glorious life, which I dare not try to describe. Earthly eyes cannot look upon the holiness, which enfolds all celestial things. Suffice it to say, that no joy known on earth – however rare, however sacred – can be more than the faintest shadow of the joy we find in heaven.

No earthly dreams of rapture come close to the bliss of even one moment in that divine world. There is no sorrow, pain, sickness, or death; no disappointments – no tears but those of joy; no broken hopes or mislaid plans; no night, nor storm – not even shadows. There is light and joy; there is love, peace, and rest - forever and forever. "Amen," and again my heart says reverently, "Amen."

Chapter 8

I have fond memories of the morning that I heard my name being called in affectionate tones. I turned and saw a tall, fine-looking man walking toward me. His uncovered head was silvery white, and his deep blue eyes looked happily and tenderly into mine, as he came closer to me.

"Oliver!" I cried with outstretched hands of welcome. "Dear, dear Oliver!" It was my oldest sister's husband, whom I had always dearly loved.

Grasping my hands warmly, he said: "I am so delighted to have you here. Your father told me, only a few moments ago, that you had come. It seems more like the old life to see you than any of the others, because we were together so often during the last few years. Would you like to see the home I've built for your sister?"

Oliver continued, "I was thinking - only a few days ago – about how much I would like you to be here before Beth comes, because you know her tastes so well. It is surprising how often our unspoken wishes are fulfilled in heaven!"

"I have also found that to be true," I said. "And, yes, I would love to see the home you have prepared for Beth. Is my sister coming soon?"

"That I cannot confidently say, but you know the years of the earth-life are passing quickly. Her coming cannot be delayed for very much longer. Can you come with me now?"

"Gladly," I said, turning to walk with him.

"It is only a short distance from here, just where the river bends. I chose that spot, because Beth loves the water so."

"This is truly charming!" I cried, as we came closer to their home. "I have not been this way before."

"I want you to see the river from the windows in her room," he said. "I know you will enjoy it."

We entered the beautiful house, which was built from the purest white granite. It was so deeply embedded in the foliage of the flower-laden trees that – from some points of view – only glimpses of its fine symmetry could be seen.

"She loves flowers so much – will she not enjoy these trees?" he asked, with almost boyish delight.

"Beyond anything she could have imagined," I answered.

We passed through several delightful rooms on the lower floor. Ascending the graceful stairway, we entered the room he was so anxious for me to see. I stopped at the entrance with an exclamation of delight! He stood watching the expression on my face with heartfelt enjoyment.

"It is one of the most delightful rooms I have ever seen!" I cried enthusiastically. Frameworks of the sofas, chairs, and desk were made from pure and spotless pearl, and were covered with a luxurious fabric of glistening gold; soft rugs and draperies accented the room perfectly. Through the beautiful glass doors, which opened upon the flower-wreathed balcony, was a view so captivating that I again caught my breath in delight. The tranquil waters of the river below reflected a thousand exquisite tints from the heavens above. A floating boat was perfectly mirrored in the placid water.

Far across the shining river, the celestial hills arose with domes, pillared temples, and sparkling fountains that danced in the glorious light. When at last I turned from this panoramic view, I saw the same divine face smiling down upon me that I daily looked upon in my own room.

We descended the stairway in silence, and then I could only

say hesitantly, "No place but heaven could provide such perfection in everything!" Oliver pressed my hand lovingly and let me leave without saying another word.

Many months, by earthly time, had passed since that day. I had often visited that lovely home and held sweet conversations with this brother I loved so dearly. I could suggest nothing that would add to the beauty of this "work of love", but we talked about it together. We planned for - and anticipated - the joy of Beth's coming.

One day I found that Oliver was gone. Although I waited for him to return, he did not come. I had not seen him for several days and concluded that the Master had sent him upon some mission.

As I walked toward my home, I met a group of happy girls and boys of different ages. They were hurrying toward the direction from which I had just come. Their arms were full of exquisitely beautiful flowers.

As they came closer, I saw that they were the grandchildren of my dear sister: Timothy, Mary, David, Lee, and little Abigail. As soon as they saw me, with one voice, they began to shout joyfully, "Grandma is coming! Grandma is coming! We are taking flowers to scatter everywhere!"

"How do you know she is coming? I have just been to the house, and no one is there."

"But she is coming," said little Lee. "We had a message from grandpa, and he has gone to get her."

"I will go and tell the others. We will all come to welcome her," I said.

With a great joy in my heart, I hurried toward my father's house. I found my family waiting for me, filled with joyful expectation.

"Yes, we have also heard," said my father. "We were waiting for you to return, so we could go together."

"I will go and get Robert, so he may also go with us," I said.

"I am here," said a cheerful voice. Looking up, I saw Robert standing at the door.

"Colonel Stratton is always wherever he is needed," said my father warmly.

It was a large, happy group that left my parent's house that day, to welcome this dearly loved one to her home: my father, mother, and sister; my brother (the doctor) and his two pretty daughters; my Aunt Grace, her son and his wife and daughter; my brother Robert and I.

As we approached the house, we heard the sound of joyful voices. We looked inside and saw my sister with her husband's arm around her. The happy grandchildren gathered around them, like hummingbirds among the flowers.

As I moved closer, I could hardly believe what I saw. Could this radiant creature - with smooth skin and happy eyes - be the pale woman, so crushed with suffering and sorrow that I had last seen? I looked with eager eyes. Yes! It was my sister, but as she was over thirty years ago. She had the beauty of health upon her face, and the light of youth in her tender eyes.

I withdrew into the shadow of the vines and let the others precede me, because my heart was filled with an extraordinary triumphant joy. This truly was the "victory over death" that was so surely promised by our risen Lord.

I watched the happy greetings, and the way she took each loved one into her arms. One by one, she greeted and embraced them. I saw her, with a curious "tugging" at my heart, turn and longingly look around. She whispered to my father: "Is not my Sara here?"

I could wait no longer. Hurrying to her side, I cried, "Dear sister, I am here! Welcome! Welcome!"

She folded me to her heart and held me tightly in her warm arms. She showered me with little kisses upon my head, while I returned each loving touch. I laughed and cried with such gladness that she had come at last. Oh, what a family reunion there was within our heavenly home! Its bliss was heightened by the sure knowledge (not the hope) that we would be together throughout all eternity!

Oliver looked on with proud and happy eyes. The hour for which he had longed and waited had come to him at last; his home-life would now forever be complete.

With a grin, I asked whether Beth had found the new house to be satisfactory. Oliver smiled and said, "She had looked at, and very greatly admired the house, before she knew it was our home."

"What did she do when she saw her lovely room?"

"She held me and cried like a child," then said, 'this repays us many times over for the lost home of earth!' If the children had not come, I think she would still be there, looking at the view of the river," he stated, laughing happily.

"I am so glad you could be alone with her when she arrived," I whispered. "You deserve that happiness, dear Oliver." He smiled gratefully and looked over at his wife, who was standing in the center of a happy group.

"Doesn't she look very young to you?" I asked.

"The years rolled away from her like a mask, as we sat beneath the water in the river. We truly do renew our youth in those life-giving waters, but her transformation was immediate and quite extraordinary."

"Her coming has also brought youth to you," I said, noticing his fresh complexion and sparkling eyes. "I hope it will not change your silver hair, though, for that is your crown of glory."

He looked at me carefully, for a moment, and then said: "I wonder if you realize the change that has also come to you in this wonderful place."

"To me?" I asked, a little surprised at his statement. "I realize what – through the Father's mercy – this life has done for me spiritually; but as for the other, I don't think I have given it a moment's thought."

"The change is as great in your case as in Beth's - although with you, the change was more gradual," he said.

I felt a sweet thrill of joy with the realization that, when my dear husband came, he would find me with the freshness and attractiveness of our earlier years. It was a precious thought, and my heart was filled with gratitude to the Father for this further evidence of His loving care.

As we all talked, the hours melted away. My father finally said, "Come, children; we must not forget that this dear daughter of mine needs rest on the first day in her new home. Let us leave her and her happy husband to their new-found bliss." With light hearts we went our way, and left them alone to begin their heavenly lives with each other.

Heaven

Chapter 9

After an enjoyable visit with family members at my parent's home, my brother hurried away to carry out an important mission, while I walked on alone toward the sacred lake. I felt a desire to rest in its soothing waters after the exciting scenes through which I had passed.

Prior to this time, I had visited the lake in the early morning hours. It was now well into the afternoon of the heavenly day, and few people lingered on the shore. The boats that raced across its calm surface seemed to be filled with individuals who were intent upon some mission, rather than those simply seeking pleasure.

I walked slowly down into the water and soon found myself floating in mid-current. The prismatic rays that in the early morning were such a wonder, now blended into a golden glory. There were different shades of rose and purple, flashing their splendor from side to side. It seemed even more beautiful to me than the rainbow tints, just as the more fleeting pleasures of youth pale by comparison to the more mature joys of our earthly lives. I could only wonder what its evening glories would be like, and resolved to come during some glowing twilight. I wanted to see if they would remind me of the calm hours of life's closing day.

I heard the chimes from the silver bell in the great city playing a song as I lay in the water, and its notes seemed to ring clearly: "Holy! Holy! Holy! Lord God Almighty!" The waters joined the song and a thousand waves around me responded, "Holy! Holy! Holy!" The notes seemed to "vibrate" upon the waves, producing a wondrously harmonious effect.

The front row of advancing waves softly proclaimed, "Holy" as it passed onward; immediately the following row of waves took over where the first seemed to have dropped off as it echoed the second, "Holy" in the divine chorus. Then, this row passed onward to take up the next note as the third advancing column caught the first; and so it passed and echoed from wave to wave, until it seemed as though millions of tiny waves around me had taken up and were delivering their part in this grand crescendo – this wonderful anthem.

Language fails me – I cannot hope to convey to others this experience as it came to me. It was majestic, wonderful, and inspiring. I lay and listened until my whole being was filled with the divine melody. It seemed as though I, too, was a part of the great chorus. I lifted my voice and joined wholeheartedly in the thrilling song of praise.

I found that, contrary to my usual practice, I floated rapidly away from the shore where I had entered the water. After a time, I realized that I was approaching a portion of the lakeshore I had never visited.

Refreshed and invigorated, I climbed the sloping banks and found myself in the midst of a lovely suburban village. It was similar to the one where our home was situated. There were some differences in the architecture and construction of the houses, though they were no less beautiful than others I had seen. Many were constructed of highly polished woods. They resembled the finest chalets one would see in Switzerland, though far surpassing them in all that gives pleasure to the artistic eye.

As I wandered farther, delighting in the lovely views around me, I was especially impressed by the appearance of an unusually attractive cottage. Its broad terraces almost hung over the waters of the lake, the wide low steps running along one side of the house to the water's edge. Several graceful swans were leisurely drifting with the current. A bird that was similar to our Southern mocking-bird was singing and swinging in the low branches overhead. There were many larger and more imposing villas nearby, but none possessed the charm of this sweet home.

Beneath one of the large flowering trees, I saw a woman who was sitting and weaving with her delicate hands. She apparently used no instrument or needle, as she created a snow-white, gossamer-like fabric that fell into a soft, fleecy pile at her side as she worked. She was so very small in stature that, at first glance, I supposed she was a child. After looking more closely, however, I saw that she was a mature woman, though with the glow of youth still upon her smooth cheeks.

Something familiar in her movements, rather than her appearance, caused me to feel that it was not the first time we had met. I was beginning to grow accustomed to the delightful surprises I discovered everywhere in this world of rare delights. I drew near her to speak, but before I could say a word, she looked up – and the doubt was gone.

"Maggie!" "Mrs. Stratton!" we cried simultaneously. She dropped her work and stepped up quickly to greet me.

Our greeting was warm and enthusiastic. Her sweet face glowed with a welcome that reminded me of the happy days when we had first met, many years ago, by the shore of a beautiful lake in the world of our earth-life.

"Now I know why I came this way today, dear," I said, as we sat side by side. We talked as we had never talked on earth, for much of the shyness of her human life had melted away in the balmy air of heaven.

"What are you making from this lovely fabric you are weaving?" I asked, lifting the silken, fleecy creation in my fingers as I spoke.

"Some draperies for Eve's room," she said. "You know the two of us lived together for so long, I thought it would seem more like home to her if we did the same here. This cottage is our own special home, just a few steps from Marie's" – she pointed to an impressive house a few yards away – "and I am decorating it as daintily as I can, especially Eve's room."

"Oh, let me help you, Maggie dear," I said. "It would bring such pleasure to me."

She hesitated an instant, with something similar to the old-time shyness, then said: "That is so like you, dear Mrs. Stratton. If you would truly enjoy it, I would love to have your help decorating the house. I have set my heart on doing Eve's room entirely by myself – there is no hurry you know – but I would be delighted to have your assistance with the other rooms."

"Will you teach me how to weave these delicate hangings?"

"Yes, indeed. Shall I give you your first lesson now?"

Lifting the dainty thread, she showed me how to toss and wind it through my fingers until it fell away in shining folds. It was very light and fascinating work, and I was soon weaving it almost as rapidly as she did.

"You are a bright scholar," said Maggie, laughing happily. "What a charming hour you have given me!"

"What a charming hour you have given me, my dear!" I answered.

When we parted, it was with the understanding that I was to often repeat the visit. When I urged her to do likewise, she said: "Here we shall be entirely alone. You come to me."

I agreed, since in heaven we never seek to gain reluctant consent for any pleasure – however dear – and many were the happy hours spent with her in the cottage by the lake.

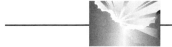

Chapter 10

One glorious morning, as my sister and I were sitting upon the upper terrace of her lovely home, she said to me: "I often look across the river to those lovely hills in the distance, and wonder if it is all as beautiful there as it is here. I would like to go there someday to see."

"Why not today?" I asked.

"Could you go with me this morning?" she responded, as she turned her radiant face again toward the river and the lovely fields beyond.

"With pleasure," I replied. "I have often wished to go myself. There is something very inviting about the beautiful landscape beyond the river. Where is Oliver?" I asked. "Will he not go with us?"

Looking smilingly toward me she said, "No, he has gone upon an important mission for the Master today; but you and I can go and return before he does."

"Then let us do so," I answered, rising and taking her hand.

Instead of turning toward the stairway in the center of the building, we walked deliberately toward the low wall that surrounded the upper balcony. Without a moment's hesitation, we stepped over the wall and into the sweet air that surrounded us.

There was no fear of falling; there was no fear of anything in this wonderful place, because we absolutely knew we were safe at all times. Our feet were as secure as they would have been, had they touched the solid earth.

We had the power of passing through the air at will, swiftly and securely, as though a boat upon the waters were carrying us. We could also navigate through water as easily as we could walk upon the crystal paths and green lawns around us.

We ascended slightly until we were just above the treetops, and then – what shall I say? We did not fly, and we made no effort with our hands or feet. *Drifting* is the only word that comes to mind, which could describe this wonderful experience.

We moved as a leaf or a feather floats through the air on a balmy day, and the sensation was most delightful. We saw the little children playing and the people walking beneath us, through the green foliage of the trees.

As we neared the river, we looked down upon the pleasure-boats that were moving across the water. We also noticed several people who were sitting, lying, or walking on the pebbly bottom of the river; we saw them with the same clarity that we would have, had we simply looked at them through the atmosphere.

Talking as we drifted onward, we were soon over the tops of the hills, which we had so longingly viewed from the terrace of my sister's home. For some time, we had no words to exchange; our hearts were filled with sensations that only the scenes of heaven can inspire. When this silence was finally broken, my sister quoted from one of the old earth-hymns:

> *Sweet fields beyond the swelling flood,*
> *Stand dressed in living green.*

In the same spirit, I answered:

> *It is indeed a rapturous scene*
> *That rises to our sight,*
> *Sweet fields arrayed in living green,*
> *And rivers of delight.*

In looking down, we began to see many suburban villages. Among many of them there was an unfamiliar environment, and the architecture of the buildings seemed quite different from our own.

I suggested to my sister that we drop downward. As we did this, we soon realized what had caused this distinction in the architecture and surroundings. Where our homes were situated, people of our nationality that we had known and loved for many years in the earth-life surrounded us. Many of these villages were formed from what appeared to be foreign nations. Each village retained some of the characteristics of its own earth-life, which were unfamiliar to us.

As we continued to drift forward, we passed over an exquisitely beautiful valley that was located between low hills of luxuriant green vegetation. We saw a group of people seated upon the ground in a semicircle. There seemed to be hundreds of them, and in their midst was a man who was apparently talking to them. Something familiar, and yet unfamiliar, in the scene attracted us. "Shall we go nearer so we can hear what he is saying and see who these people are?" I asked.

"Oh, yes," my sister replied.

When we did this, we found that the people slightly resembled some of our own Native American tribes. Their clothing was similar to that worn upon earth, although they were even more beautiful. The faces, with intense interest depicted on each, were turned toward the man who was talking to them. As we looked more closely, we saw that he was Caucasian. In a whisper of surprise I said to my sister, "Why, he is a missionary."

As so often seemed to happen when a surprise or a question surfaced, there was someone near to answer and enlighten us. We found on this occasion that our instructor was beside us, ready to give us any information we desired.

He responded, "Yes, you are right. This is a missionary who gave his life to tell others about Jesus. He spent many years working for them and teaching those who had not heard the truth. The result, as you see before you, was that hundreds of people were brought into the Master's kingdom. They gather around him daily and he leads them higher and higher into the blessed life."

"Are there others like him in this beautiful realm?" I asked.

"Many hundreds," he said. "All of us have much yet to learn of this wonderful life."

As we continued our journey and floated above other villages, we were often delighted by songs of praise rising from the churches, and from people gathered together in various groups. In many cases, to our surprise, the hymns and the words were those with which we had been familiar on earth. Although they were being sung in a different language, we understood every word. That was another of the wonderful surprises of heaven. There was no language that we could not understand.

On, and on, and on – through wonderful scenes of beauty we passed. We finally returned to our own homes, but from a different direction than we had left. It seemed as though we had made a circle in our pleasant journeying. When I left my sister at her home, she whispered to me, "It has been a day of such wonderful rest and pleasure that we must soon repeat it together."

"Yes, dear," I answered, "we certainly will!"

Chapter 11

On one of my walks, I happened to come upon a scene that brought to mind some comments Mae had made about the Savior's love for little children. I found Him sitting beneath one of the flowering trees upon the lakeshore, with about a dozen children of different ages clustered around Him.

One dainty little girl, not more than a year old, was cradled in His arms. Her sunny head rested confidently upon His chest, and her tiny hands were filled with some of the lovely water lilies that were so abundant in that heavenly place. She was too young to realize what a great honor it was to be held by the Master, but seemed to be extremely happy in His care.

The others sat contentedly at His feet or leaned upon His knees. One dear little boy - with serious eyes – stood, while resting his head upon the Master's shoulder. Each child was attentively focused upon Jesus and appeared to be listening carefully to His words. He seemed to be telling them a story, which had been adapted to their level of interest and ability to understand.

I sat down upon the grass among a group of people, who were some distance from the little ones that surrounded the Savior. We were too far away to catch more than a sentence now and then, however, and in heaven one never intrudes upon another's privileges or pleasures. We simply enjoyed their young smiles, eager questions, and happy exclamations. We were able to gather some of the story's meaning from the sentences that "floated" to us.

We heard the Master say – in response to the questioning looks of the interested children – "A small child lost in the dark woods of the lower world."

A while later we heard, "Wild lions and bears."

"Where was his papa?" asked a little girl.

We could not hear the reply, but soon a boy who was leaning upon the Savior's knee said confidently, "No dangerous lions and bears up here!"

"No," Jesus replied, "there is never anything that would harm or frighten anyone here!"

As the story deepened and became more exciting, they all gathered closer around the Master. He turned with a loving smile – and we could see Him place His arm around the little boy with the serious eyes as He asked, "Peter, what would you have done?"

With a bright light in his eyes and a flush on his fair cheeks, the child answered quickly and emphatically: "I would have prayed to You and asked You to close the lion's mouth, as You did for Daniel, and You would have done it!"

I thought, "If only Peter's parents could see the look the beloved Master gave their son as he made his brave reply, they would be comforted even in the absence of their dear boy."

Lost in these thoughts, I heard no more that was said until an ecstatic shout from the children announced that the story had ended satisfactorily. Looking up, I saw the Savior leaving with the baby still in His arms. The other children were marching triumphantly around Him.

I, too, arose and started walking toward home. I had not gone far before I met Robert, who greeted me by saying, "I am on my way to the city by the lake; would you like to come with me?"

"Yes, I would very much like to go with you. It has been my wish to visit the city. I only waited until you thought it would be wise for me to go," I answered.

"You are growing so fast in the knowledge of the heavenly ways," he said, "that I think I would take you almost anywhere with me now. You acquire the knowledge for the very love of it; not simply because you feel it is your duty to learn. Your eagerness to gather all truth – and at the same time, your patient submission in waiting – have earned much praise and love for you from our dear Master. He eagerly watches the progress, which each of us makes in this heavenly life. I think it is only right that you should know, and I tell you with His permission. We enjoy encouragement here as much as we do in the earth-life, although in a different way."

It would be impossible for me to convey, in the language of earth, the impression these words of commendation left upon me. The praise was so unexpected. It was true that I had eagerly gathered all of the knowledge I possibly could - with a genuine love for the study of all things, which pertained to the blessed life. I had not even considered the possibility that I would receive any type of praise for doing so. The realization that I had won the approval of the Master Himself seemed almost too wonderful to comprehend.

"My brother, my dear brother," was all I could say, stopping suddenly and looking up into his face with grateful tears.

"I am so glad for you, little sister," he said, warmly clasping my hand. "I think it will not be long before the Master entrusts you with a mission. There are, you see, rewards in heaven. I am delighted that you have unconsciously earned one of these so soon."

I wish I could write the precious words of wisdom that fell from my brother's lips. I wish that I could describe the events of that wonderful life precisely as they were unfolded to me day by day; but I can only say, "I may not."

When I decided to make a record of that never-to-be forgotten time, I did not realize how many serious difficulties I would encounter; how often I would have to pause and consider whether or not I could reveal this truth, or paint that scene, as it appeared to me. The very *heart* has often been left out of some of the wonderful scenes I have attempted to describe, because I found that I dared not reveal their sacred mysteries. I am painfully aware that the narrative, as I am compelled to give it, falls infinitely short of what I had originally hoped to record. Please bear with me, though, for it is no frivolous sketch I am portraying; but rather the life beyond, as it appeared to me.

My brother and I walked slowly back to the edge of the lake, where we stepped into a boat that was beached upon the lakeshore. I never knew by what power these boats were propelled; there were no oarsmen, no engines, or sails.

As the boat moved steadily forward, I admired the luxuriously cushioned seats. I noticed a musical instrument laying on one of them that was somewhat like a violin, but had no bow. Could it be that none was required? As though answering my unspoken question, Robert gently lifted the instrument and, using only his fingers, began to play a soothing – yet, at the same time, exhilarating – refrain.

When he had finished playing, my brother leaned back to relax. I was drawn to a book on the cushion beside me and noticed that it appeared to be the continuation of a Christian book I had read on earth. As I glanced through it, I realized that this great author had addressed many of the mighty eternal issues and had provided insight to those in heaven, even as he had to those in the past life.

My thoughts were interrupted when the boat came to rest at a marble terrace. Disembarking, we walked up a slight incline and found ourselves in a wide street that led into the heart of the city. *

I discovered that the streets were all very wide and smooth. They were paved with marble and precious stones of every kind. Though they were crowded with people who were involved with various duties, not an atom of debris – or even dust – was visible anywhere.

There seemed to be vast business buildings of many kinds. There were numerous colleges and schools; art galleries, museums, and libraries; large concert halls and auditoriums; book and music stores; publishing houses; and several large, manufacturing sites – including those where the fine, silk threads of numerous colors were spun. (These were used extensively in the weaving of the draperies I have already mentioned.)

There may have been people living in the city, but I noticed no residences until we came to the suburbs. The houses stood in great magnificence and splendor. Every home had a large yard filled with trees, flowers, and pleasant walkways; indeed, it was like one vast park that was dotted with lovely homes.

As we continued to walk, we came to a very large park that had many lovely features: walks, fountains, miniature lakes, and shaded seats. It had no dwellings or buildings with the exception of an immense, circular, open temple. My brother told me that an angel choir assembled here daily to perform the great musical oratorios.

The choir had just left, but the crowd who had enjoyed the divine music still lingered – as though they were reluctant to leave so holy a spot. "We will remember the hour," my brother said, "and come again when we can hear them."

There was much that charmed, much that surprised me in this great city – of which I may not fully speak, but will never forget.

* This city is not to be confused with the *New Jerusalem* and its golden streets, which will not be revealed until a later time, as described in Revelation, Chapter 21.

Chapter 12

Still passing through the park, we came out upon the open country. We walked quite a distance through flowery meadows and grassy fields, in which the gently blowing wind produced a wave-like effect. After some time, we entered a great forest with huge trees that towered above us like softly swaying giants. The day was coming to an end – a day that had been filled to overflowing with joy, glad surprises, and happy hours!

As full as it had been, I felt there was still something left for me, hidden deeply in the twilight-valley of the day; something that held my soul in awe, as the last moments preceding the Holy Communion.

My brother walked by me, absorbed in silent thought, but with a touch beyond even his usual gentleness. I did not ask where we were going at that late hour. Even though we were far from home, no fear, doubt, or questioning disturbed the quietness of my soul. Although the forest was dense, the golden glow of the twilight rested beneath the trees. The radiance sifted down through the swaying overhead branches, as though falling through the windows of some grand cathedral.

We eventually emerged from the forest upon an extensive plain that stretched out into a limitless space before us. We could faintly hear the distant thunder of the breaking waves from the eternal sea, which I had often heard about, but had not yet seen. Other than the faint and distant echo of the waves, the silence around us was intense. We stood a moment upon the border of the forest, crossed a small bridge, and then advanced a few steps into the plain.

I became aware of the fact that, to our right, the ground was quite elevated; and as I turned, a sight came into view that the eternal years of earth and heaven can never erase. A majestic Temple* was positioned at the highest point of this extensive slope; its ornate dome, massive pillars, and solid walls were of pure sculpted pearl. A white radiance shone through the towering windows that swallowed up the golden glow of the twilight and made it its own.

I did not cry aloud nor hide my face, as I had during past revelations. I sank slowly to my knees and crossed my hands upon my chest. With uplifted face, stilled heart, and silent lips, I placed my whole being in worship at His feet . . .

How long I knelt, I do not know. Even immortal life seemed to fade away before that greatest of celestial mysteries. Ultimately, my brother who had been kneeling silently beside me arose – and lifting me to my feet – whispered gently, "Come." I yielded to his guidance in silence.

A long flight of solid pearl steps ascended to the doors of the Temple. On each side of the stairway, crystal clear streams flowed over beds of shimmering diamonds and gold, descending exquisitely – through a series of small, beautiful waterfalls. Farther out upon the plain, the two streams joined to become a river.

We climbed the steps to enter the Temple and stood, for a moment, in silence. In that brief instant, every detail of that wonderful interior was embedded upon my memory, as a scene is photographed upon the artist's canvas. Prior to this time, it had taken repeated visits to a room before I could describe it correctly in detail. In a lightning's flash, however, this was stamped upon my

Please note that the Temple depicted here is not within the city called the New Jerusalem (as described in Revelation 21) in which there will be no Temple.

memory for all time – not as we count time on earth, rather for all eternity.

The interior of the enormous dome was filled with a glowing cloud and was supported by three rows of massive golden pillars. They stood like rows of watchmen upon the shining floor.

The walls and floors were solid pearl, as was the great platform that filled at least one-third of the eastern side of the Temple. There were no seats of any kind. A railing of gold circled around the platform on three sides, so that it was inaccessible from the body of the Temple. Beneath the gold railing, upon the Temple-floor, a pearl kneeling-step proceeded around the platform.

An immense altar of gold arose from the center of the platform and was supported at each corner by huge, golden angels with outspread wings. Under the alter, in a great pearl basin, sparkling water danced in a fountain. I knew intuitively that this was the source of the river that flowed through the gardens of heaven and removed the last remnants of the earth-life from our bodies.

Four angels dressed in flowing, white garments stood on the platform. Long, slim trumpets of gold were lifted in their hands, as though they were expectantly awaiting the signal for their trumpet call.

Long draperies of exquisite, filmy fabric hung in heavy folds behind the altar platform. Suddenly, at the very moment we looked, the draperies trembled and glowed until a radiance – far beyond the splendor of the sun at midday – shone through them. The whole Temple was filled with the glory of the Lord.

We saw, in the midst of the glowing cloud that filled the dome, the forms of angelic harpists. As we dropped with bowed heads beside the altar, and hid our faces from the "brightness of His coming," we heard the trumpet-call of the four angels who were standing on the platform. The voices of the celestial harpists sang:

Holy, Holy, Holy, Lord God Almighty!
All thy works shall praise thy name, in earth, and sky, and sea,
Holy, Holy, Holy, merciful and mighty,
God in three persons – blessed Trinity. Amen!

The voices softly faded away, the last notes of the golden trumpets sounded, and there was silence in heaven. We knew that the visible glory of the Lord was, for the present, withdrawn from the Temple.

We continued to kneel, with bowed heads, in silent worship. When at last we arose, I did not lift my eyes while within the Temple; I wanted it to remain upon my memory, as it had appeared when it was filled with His glory.

We walked for some time in silence. I leaned upon my brother's arm, for I yet trembled with emotion. As I began to recall each detail of this most holy time, I was impressed by the realization that there are no denominations in heaven. Everyone worships together in harmony and love – the children of one loving Father.

"What a shame that this aspect of heaven could not be understood and practiced by the inhabitants of earth," I thought. There would be no petty denominational arguments, jealousies, and rivalries - no building of one church or denomination upon the ruins or downfall of another; rather, one great universal brotherhood whose head is Christ and whose cornerstone is Love.

I was surprised to see that we did not return to the forest, but went farther upon the plain. When I saw that we were approaching the area where the streams united, I understood that we would return by way of the river, rather than by forest and lake.

We finally reached the river and stepped into a boat near the shore. We were soon floating with the current toward our home. We passed through much beautiful scenery that I had not previously seen. I resolved that I would return in the future, when leisure from my daily duties permitted.

Lovely villas were surrounded by beautiful grounds, which stretched directly up from the water's edge on both sides of the river. They formed a panorama that was so lovely one would never become tired of the view.

Toward the end of the journey, we passed my sister's lovely home. We could clearly see her and her husband drinking in the scene, with intense delight, from the doorway of her special room.

My brother and I were both silent during most of the journey homeward. We each noted, however, the signs of happy family life that surrounded us on every side. Here and there, cheerful inhabitants could be seen on the terraces and steps of the homes we passed; glad voices could often be heard, and merry shouts of laughter came from the groups of little children playing upon the flowery lawns.

I broke our silence by saying to my brother, "I have often been delightfully surprised to hear the familiar songs of earth reproduced in heaven, but never more so than I was today. That hymn has long been a favorite of mine."

"These happy surprises do not come by chance," he answered. "One of the delights of this rare life is that no occasion is ever overlooked for reproducing the pure enjoyments of our earthly lives. It is the Father's pleasure to bring to our recognition, the fact that this existence is but a continuance of the former life, only without its imperfections and cares."

"Robert, I believe you are the only one who has never questioned me about the dear ones left behind; why is that?"

He gave me an especially happy smile as he answered, "Perhaps it is because I already know more than you could tell me."

"I wondered if it were not so," I said. I remembered my dear father saying – in speaking of my brother on the first day of my coming – "He stands very near to the Master." I also knew how often he was sent upon missions to the world below.

After our return, I reclined on my sofa. My heart overflowed with joy, gratitude, and love beyond the power of expression. It seemed to me that the tenderness in the divine eyes looking down upon me from the wall was deeper, purer, and more holy than it had ever been.

"I will reach the standard of perfection You have set for me, my Savior," I whispered hesitantly - with clasped hands uplifted to Him. "I will do this if it takes my eternal life in heaven and help from all the angels of light to accomplish it." With these words upon my lips and His tender eyes watching over me, I sank into the blissful rest of heaven.

Chapter 13

So much occurred – and so rapidly - from the very hour I entered the heavenly realm, it is impossible for me to transcribe it in its entirety. Of the many dear friends I met, only a few have been mentioned. These meetings are similar in many respects, so I have tried to describe those incidents that would be representative of daily life in that beautiful world; to clearly portray the admiration and love all hearts feel toward the blessed Trinity, and to convey the marvelous power of Christ's love.

This world, so strange and new to me, held multitudes of those I had loved in the years gone by. There was rarely a day in which friendships that had seemed to be broken, when loved ones left the earthly life, were not renewed.

One afternoon, as I was walking in the neighborhood of Mrs. Harris's home, I was attracted to a very picturesque house. It was nearly hidden by thick, lush, climbing rose-vines. The flowers were creamy white, and their beauty surpassed that of any roses I had seen on earth or in heaven.

Meeting Mrs. Harris, I pointed to the house and asked, "Who lives there?"

"Perhaps you should go over and see," she said.

"Is it anyone I know?"

"Yes, it is. See, someone is waiting at the door, as though she is expecting you."

I hurried over the white walk and flowery lawn. Before I could climb the steps, I found myself in the loving arms of my dear Aunt Anne.

"Sara Stratton! I was sure it was you when I saw you go to see Mrs. Harris a day or two ago. Did she not tell you I was here?"

"She had no opportunity until today," I said. "But dear Aunt Anne, I would have found you soon; surely you know that."

"Yes, my dear niece – of course, I do."

Then, I talked to her about my first encounter with the Master. She listened, her dear face full of understanding, and said, "Dear, you need not tell me anymore – do I not know? When the Master comes to me, I have no thought or care for anything beyond that, for many blissful hours! Oh – the joy, the peace of knowing I am safe in this blessed haven. How far beyond all of our earthly dreams is this divine life."

She sat for a moment lost in thought, then said hopefully, "Now, tell me of my children. Are they coming soon?"

I cheered her heart with news of her loved ones, as we talked the hours away. We recalled many sweet memories of the earth-life – of friends, home, and family ties; and looked forward to the future coming of those we love so dearly.

A few days later, as the soft twilight began to fall, many of our precious family members were gathered with us in the great "flower room." We heard steps on the terrace, and as my brother went to the open door a gentle voice said, "Is Mrs. Stratton really here?"

"She is really here. Come and see for yourself," and sweet Mary Green entered the room.

"I am so glad to welcome you home!" she said, coming to me with extended hands and expressive eyes.

"My precious girl," I cried, taking her to my heart in a warm embrace. "I have been asking about you and longing to see you."

"I could hardly wait to come when I heard that you were here. Now, tell me everything – everything!" she said, as I drew her to a seat close beside me. Every individual member of her dear home-circle was discussed.

"I was often so close that I could have touched you with my hand," she said. She described many incidents to me that had occurred when her mother and I were together on earth, talking of the dear child we considered to be far removed from our presence.

After a long, meaningful conversation between the two of us, I took her to the library - where my family had gone to examine a new book my brother had received that day. I introduced her to them as the daughter of dear friends still on earth, and was confident of the warm welcome she would receive.

She and my youngest sister quickly became friends, finding they had many mutual interests. I was happy to realize that it was likely they would see much of each other as they pursued future activities together.

Chapter 14

There was no measurement of time as we measure it here, although many still spoke in the old-time language of "months" and "years." I have no way of explaining time, as it seemed to me then. There were allotted times for happy duties, hours for joyful pleasures, and periods of holy praise. I only know it was all harmony, joy, and peace – at all times and in all ways. The current of my life flowed on - until what seemed like many wonderful years had passed.

I continued to advance in my daily studies of the heavenly mysteries. Amazingly, these very enjoyable studies were always challenging, yet never difficult. Much of what I learned was gained simply through observation, during the journeys that I took with my brother into different parts of the heavenly kingdom.

I never lacked time for social pleasures and enjoyments. There was never a conflict between duties and preferences; no unfulfilled desires, and no vain strivings for the unattainable, as there is in the life of earth.

Many precious hours of conversation were spent in my dear father's home. On a few occasions, he allowed me to assist him with instructing those who had recently arrived, regarding their duties and responsibilities in the new life.

On one of these occasions he said to me, "I have the most challenging problem I have ever had to deal with in this work. My assignment is to educate and help a man, who suddenly plunged from living an honorable life into the very depths of crime. I have never been able to convince him to go with me to the river, where these shameful memories will be swept from his mind.

His excuse has always been that God's mercy is great in allowing him inside heaven's gates, and he is content to remain forever at its lowest level of enjoyment and life. No persuasion or teaching so far has been able to make him change his decision.

He was led astray by his infatuation with an evil woman. He killed his aged mother, so he could obtain her jewels for this contemptible person. He was put to death for the crime, of which he sincerely repented; but he left life with all the horror of this despicable act holding tightly to his soul."

"Has he seen his mother since coming here? Does she know of his arrival?"

"No, I decided that it would be better not to tell her of his coming until his soul was in an improved condition to receive her. He was an only child and does not lack the elements of refinement.

He was completely under the control of the wicked - though fascinating – woman, who drugged his wine and then urged him to commit this horrible crime. She hated his mother, because his mother tried to use her influence to convince her son to leave this immoral woman.

When he became sober, he was horrified at what he had done. His infatuation for the woman turned to disgust, but it was too late. He refused to see her during his entire incarceration."

"How long was he in prison?"

"Almost a year."

"Has he seen the Christ?"

"No, he begs *not* to see him. He is very repentant and grateful to be saved from the wrath he feels was his just punishment. Though he is conscious that his sin is forgiven, he does not feel that he can ever stand in the presence of the Holy One. Here, as upon earth, each individual must be willing to receive Him; His presence is never given unless it is desired.

I have not appealed for higher help. My hope is that we can lead these souls upward through the strength that has been given to us. Can you suggest anything that might reach him?"

"I think he needs to see his mother."

He thought reflectively for a moment, and then said, "Yes, I think you are right. Your suggestion is a wise one."

We found the man's mother and placed the facts gently before her. There was no hesitancy upon her part. In an instant, she said, "My poor, poor boy. Certainly, I will go with you at once."

With great anticipation, we led her to the home where these "students" stayed. It was a beautiful building in the midst of a park; shaded walks, fountains, and flowers seemed to be everywhere. To one who had just been freed from earth, it seemed to be a paradise indeed; but to those of us who had tasted the greater joys of heaven, something was lacking. We missed the lovely, individual homes, the little children playing on the lawns, the music of the angel choir; it was very bland when compared to the pleasures we had experienced.

We found the young man seated beneath one of the flower-laden trees, looking through a book my father had left with him. There was a peaceful look on his face, but it was the look of patient resignation, rather than passionate joy.

His mother approached him by herself, while my father and I remained in the background. After a little time, he glanced up and saw his mother standing near him. A startled look came into his face, and he jumped to his feet. She extended her arms toward him and cried out lovingly, "John, my dear boy, come home to me – I need you, son."

With a low cry he knelt at her feet and clasped her knees, sobbing: "Mother, mother!"

She stooped down, put her tender arms around him, and kissed his bowed head. Oh, the love of a Christian mother! Here was this tender woman, sent into eternity by the hands of one who should have protected and cared for her. She was bending above her repentant son - with overflowing love shining upon him from her gentle eyes. I saw joyful tears streaming down my proud father's face, and I knew that my eyes, too, were wet.

My father had explained to the mother that the first thing needed, was to get her son to the river. We heard her say ever so caressingly, "Come, John, take this first step for your mother's sake, so that I may have the joy of seeing you in our own home. Come, John, dear boy."

She gently coaxed him and, to our great delight, we saw him rise and go with her. Their steps led them to the river, and they walked hand in hand. As far as we could see them, she seemed to be soothing and comforting him.

"Thank God," said my father fervently. "There will be no further hesitation now - when they return he will see more clearly."

After this, by divine permission, I became my father's assistant. In this way, I was able to spend much more time enjoying his company and instruction.

Chapter 15

One evening, after returning from a distant celestial city, I sat relaxing on the balcony of our home. From where I sat, I could see glimpses of the river through the overhanging branches of the trees. I was joyfully watching happy children play upon the lawn below me.

My brother found me on the balcony, where I was enjoying the serenity of the view. He had been absent much of the time for many days, due to some earth-mission he had been given. He had not told me, as he sometimes did, where his mission had led him. I had not asked, because I felt certain he would tell me everything it was best for me to know.

For much of my heavenly life, I had often enjoyed visits to my dear ones on earth. Recently, however, my duties had involved unusual responsibility that led me daily to a distant part of the heavenly kingdom; therefore, I had not been able to visit earth for a much longer period than typically elapsed between my visits.

When last seen, all of my dear ones had seemed to be very healthy and were surrounded by earthly blessings. I had, for that reason, thrown all of my energies into the work that had been assigned to me by the Master.

My brother observed me silently, for a moment, then said gently: "I have news for you, little sister."

A thrill of ecstasy shot through me and, in an instant, I cried out joyously, "My precious husband is coming!"

He nodded his head and smiled compassionately, but did not reply at once.

"When will it be? Am I to go to him?" I asked.

He hesitated a moment before saying, "Of course you will be permitted to go."

"Oh, I must go to him! I must be the first to greet him! Perhaps it may be granted that he can see me while he is yet in his earthly body."

He shook his head at this and said, "No, dear; he will not know you."

"Why? Robert, tell me everything – including why you think, as I plainly see you do, that it is not best for me to go."

"He became ill very suddenly, in the middle of his work-day, while apparently in perfect health. He has not regained consciousness since; nor will he ever do so on earth.

"When was this?"

"Three days ago; I have been with him almost constantly - day and night- since that time."

"Oh, why did you not tell me earlier?"

"I thought it would be wise to spare you from seeing him suffer, but I have come to tell you that you may go now if you still so desire."

"He will know me as soon as the struggle is past?"

"Yes, but he will be confused and weak. He will need stronger help and guidance than you could provide, and you would miss the rapture of the meeting as it would be a little later on."

"What would you have me do? You know I will submit to your wiser judgment even against the pleadings of my heart. I can wait."

"I will not say, 'do not go.' You may accompany me if you wish. I do believe, though, that after he has experienced the initial confusion of passing into the new life, and has bathed in the waters of the *River of Life*, he will be better prepared for the delightful reunion that awaits him.

"You remember what the waters did for you - how dazed and

troubled in spirit you were before you went into the river with me that morning. It is the same with all of us, but where there has been serious brain malfunction, it is even more needed than on ordinary occasions. That is the case with my brother; he will not be fully himself until the divine waters have cleansed the confusion from his brain."

"You are always right, dear brother. I will surrender to your wise advice, even though my heart cries out to rush to his side. When will you return to him?"

"Immediately. There will be little time to wait. With the coming of the morning light, we will be here. My brave-hearted, wise, little sister - the delay will be neither sorrowful nor long." He arose and, bending over me, kissed me lightly on my forehead. In a moment, he had passed out of view.

"How strange," I thought, "that even in this matter so near to my heart, I am able to yield without complaining. Father, I thank you! I thank you for the happy reunion that is coming so soon; I thank you even more, though, for the sweet submission that has grown in my life; that I can surrender to Your perfect will even when You would allow me to do otherwise."

I bowed my head and allowed myself to experience a mixture of thoughts. Was he, this dearly loved one, indeed unaware of his suffering? Oh, how I longed for the morning to be here! How could I wait for the sight of that beloved face?

Suddenly, a gentle touch rested upon my bowed head. A voice I had learned to recognize and love beyond all things in earth or heaven asked, "Have I not said, 'Though he were dead, yet shall he live'? How important are the years of separation, now that the time has come to meet again? Let us reason together," the Master said, smiling down into my uplifted face. He took my extended hand into His own and, sitting down beside me, continued:

"Let us consider what these years have done for you. Do you not feel that you are infinitely better prepared to give happiness than when you parted from the one you love?"

I nodded happily.

"Do you not realize that your understanding and purity have reached a higher level; and that, in the strength of the Father, the two of you from this point forward will walk upward together?"

Again, I happily agreed.

"Is the home-life here less attractive than it was in the earth-life?"

"No, no! A thousand times no!" I cried.

"Then there is nothing but joy in the reunion at hand?"

"Nothing but joy!" I echoed.

The Savior continued to lead, as we talked of the one that was coming soon. I opened my happy heart to Him as I described the noble life, the sacrificial work, the high aspirations, and the trustworthiness of the one I loved. I spoke of his bravery during times of misfortune, his courage in the face of painful trials and disappointments, and his forgiveness of even malicious injury. I concluded by saying, "He *lived* the Christianity many others professed. He always surpassed me in that."

The face of the Master glowed with understanding as we talked. He led me on until my spirit seemed to fly upward, as a lark in the early morning. He unfolded mysteries of the soul to me that filled my heart with rapture, but which I may not reveal.

I saw the rosy glow deepening across the sky, and realized that morning – love's morning – was already dawning for me in heaven. The Master arose and, pointing to the radiance, said, "By the time you are ready to receive them, they will be here." With a smile and a touch that communicated His blessing, He departed.

As I arose and stood with my face lifted toward the coming day, I heard the triumphant notes of the angels' choral song; and this morning, as though in unison with my thoughts, they sang:

He is risen! Hear it, ye heavens and ye children of earth! He is risen!

I lifted my voice, with joy, and joined their thrilling song. As they swept onward and the rhythm died away, I slowly descended the stairway. I crossed the lawn, admiring the ever- beautiful flowers, and sank for a moment beneath the pure waters of the river. I felt no pressure, no anxiety nor unrest - even though I knew the one for whom my soul had waited all these years was coming. The Master's presence had filled me with such calmness and peace – had prepared me so well for the great happiness before me – that nothing had the power to disrupt my serenity.

Filled with a new sense of delight, I again crossed the lawn. I stopped before entering the house, because I wanted to personally gather the flowers that would greet my dear husband upon his arrival.

After fastening some creamy-white roses on my dress, I went into the library. I refilled the golden bowl with spicy, scarlet carnations and lovingly laid a fragrant bud aside for my husband's jacket. With great care, I fixed my hair in the style he had most admired, adding a perfectly formed rosebud as the finishing touch.

Soon after I completed these tasks, I heard voices and steps. Listen! Yes, it is the same dear steps for which I had so often listened in the old home-life – the steps that had always brought gladness to my heart and sunshine into our home! *His* steps in heaven! I flew to the open doorway and, in an instant, was within the strong arms of my husband, feeling the beat of his loving heart. Was there anything more for me that heaven could hold?

My brother, with thoughtful care, left us and went upstairs. For a while, the two of us - whose lives had been so happily mingled throughout the long years of our time on earth - had time to be only in one another's company. He again took me in his arms and drew me to his heart. "This is heaven indeed!" he said.

We walked toward the "flower-room" and, at its entrance, he stood a moment -fascinated with its beauty. I began to relate its history to him, but he said, "Not now, my darling. I have only eyes and ears for you, all else in heaven must wait."

We sat and talked together as in days past, and the happy hours came and went. The day melted into the twilight glow before we realized it was nearly over.

Robert then joined us, and we showed my dear husband through the lovely house. We stood upon the broad terrace and ate some of the heavenly fruit. Then, we all sat together, where I had spent the hours waiting in the presence of the blessed Master. I told them much of what He had said to me. I described how He turned the hours, that I had anticipated would pass in lonely waiting, into triumphant rejoicing. The eyes of my dear husband were filled with tears. He pressed my hand, which he still kept in his, with tender compassion.

"Oh, darling, it is a blessed, blessed life!" I said.

"I already realize the blessedness," he replied, "for has it not given me back my brother and my wife – my precious wife?"

Early the following morning, I said to my husband and our brother, "We must go to see your parents today."

"Yes, we will go at once," they both replied.

Since the earliest days of my heavenly life, I had enjoyed frequent visits in the home of my husband's parents. As in the earth-life, they always made me feel welcome and loved. Now, we were taking to them a beloved son, and I realized how his coming would bring gladness to their hearts and home.

It was a joyful meeting, and the day was nearly over before we arose to return. "William," said his mother, fondly laying her hand upon his arm, "yours was a happy home on earth – I used to think a perfect home." With a loving glance toward me she added, "It will be far happier here."

"I am sure of that, mother. I am so blessed to have not only my dear wife, but also Robert, you, father, and Rachel" (a special niece) "to bring joy into our home."

We turned to go, but at the doorway came face to face with a favorite aunt who, in the earth-life, had been blind.

"Aunt Carole, is that you?" my husband asked.

Yes, it truly was Aunt Carole, but she no longer had to live in the darkness.

"My dear children," she exclaimed, "how wonderful it is to *see* you!"

The Master's touch had rested on her sightless eyes. Closing them to the darkness of earth, He had opened them upon the glories of heaven. What a marvelous transition! No wonder we left her singing:

Glory to Him who this miracle has brought
Filling my spirit with joy and delight!
Look! In my blindness I safely have walked
Out of the darkness and into the light!

Chapter 16

Days lengthened into weeks, weeks into months, and the months turned into years. The duties and joys of heaven grew clearer and dearer with each passing hour. Our home-life was perfect, although we eagerly looked forward to the future coming of our son and daughter-in-law, which would complete our family circle.

We had often spoken of going together to the great celestial sea, but had never seemed quite ready to do so. We realized it was one of the great mysteries of heaven, although we didn't know exactly what to expect. In that wonderful place, people rarely tried to describe heaven's glories, because words were so insufficient.

One morning, I said to my brother, "I have a strange desire to go to the sea. Do you think it is wise for us to go at this time?"

"I am glad that you want to go, as I also desire this for you. I was about to suggest that you and my brother take this blessed journey."

"Will you not come with us?"

"No, we will all go together another time, but it is best for now that the two of you go alone. I feel certain you will find it easily without me – walk through the forest until you come to the golden path, which takes you directly to the shore." We were soon on our way, enjoying the sparkling light of the glorious morning, and filled with a holy joy that we could take this special journey together.

As we walked through the forest, the golden light fell through the swaying branches overhead. Birds with gorgeous plumage and delightful songs were darting here and there. We began to hear, nearer and ever nearer, the rhythmic dashing of the waves against the shore. The sound of the waves was soon accompanied by bursts of triumphant songs and the harmony of many musical instruments. With the music lifting our spirits, we emerged from the forest, and stood silently before the overwhelming glory of the scene before us.

Can I describe it as it appeared to me that day? Never! Not until my lips can speak and your heart understand, the language of the *royal courts* above.

The ground at our feet sloped downward toward the shore, which was a golden strand many hundred feet wide. The length extended far beyond the limits of our vision in both directions. The sand caught and radiated the morning light, until it glittered and glimmered like the dust of diamonds and other precious stones. The waves, as they came and retreated in ceaseless motion, caught up this sparkling sand and carried it on their crests.

The sea spread out before us with a magnificence that surpassed description in any language. Although less radiant, it reminded me of the white glory that shone through the windows of the Temple. Beneath this, we saw – in the roll of the waves – the blue tint of the waters, which had no apparent limit to its depths or bounds.

Upon the sea's shining surface, we saw boats - which represented various nations - coming and going in many directions. In beauty of construction, these boats greatly outclassed anything earth has ever known. They were like great, open pleasure-ships that were filled with people who were eagerly looking toward the shore. Many were excitedly searching the faces of those standing and waiting at the water's edge.

Ah, the people waiting upon the shore! They stood as far as the eye could observe - a great mass of beautiful souls, clothed in shining apparel. Many among them had golden harps or various

84   Heaven

musical instruments. Whenever a boat touched the shore, joyful voices and tender embraces - from loved ones in the crowd - welcomed the travelers. The harps would then be held high, all of the golden instruments would sound, and the vast multitude would break forth into the triumphant song of victory over death and the grave.

"I wonder if these people always stand here."

"Not the same people," answered a radiant being near us, who had heard my question. "There is always a gathering of people here, though – some who are expecting friends and loved ones from the other life, and others who assemble to share their joy. The heavenly choristers are also always here, but not always the same ones. You may notice that most of those who arrive are led quietly away by their friends, and many others are constantly joining the multitude." He walked on toward the shore and left us enveloped in awe and wonder.

We soon became deeply interested in watching the reunions, and found ourselves joining in the glad songs of rejoicing. Now and then, we would get very excited - when we saw a face that we remembered seeing on earth among the eager faces in the boats. It made us notice more closely and relate more heartily, with those who welcomed beloved friends.

We would see a wife in the close embrace of a waiting husband; then, a little child would excitedly jump into the outstretched arms of her happy mother; friends hugged other friends in welcome reunion; and an aged mother was enfolded to the heart of her beloved child.

As one ship of rare strength and beauty came floating gracefully over the waves, we observed the tall figure of a man standing near her prow. His arms were encircled around a graceful woman who stood by his side. Each of them was fervently scanning and searching the faces of the crowd as the boat neared the shore. Suddenly, with a great thrill of joy surging through my being, I cried out: "It is our precious son and his dear wife! They have come together!"

In an instant, we were quickly moving through the crowd, which joyfully parted to let us pass through. As the boat touched the shore, they moved swiftly toward us. Our dear daughter-in-law found her own happy parents, who had been waiting near the edge of the water, and was being held close to their hearts.

At the same time, we felt the arms of our beloved son enfolding us; and soon thereafter we were all in each other's embrace. Oh, what a rapturous moment that was! Our lives in heaven were complete! As we stood blissfully, with our arms around one another, the heavenly choir broke into song. With uplifted faces radiant with joy, eyes filled with happy tears, and voices trembling with emotion, we all joined in the happy anthem:

> *Glory be unto the Father, and unto the Son!*
> *Glory be unto the ever-blessed Three in One!*
> *No more sorrow, no more parting, no more grief or pain;*
> *Christ has broken death's strong chains,*
> *We are free again!*
> *Heart to heart and hand to hand,*
> *Meet we on the golden strand.*
> *Glory, glory to the Father! Glory to the Son!*
> *Glory be unto the ever-blessed Three in One!*
> *Alleluia! Amen!*

The song soared and swelled triumphantly as the vast multitude joined their voices in unison. The billowing waves created a deep undertone to the melody that increased its solemnity. With bowed heads and full hearts, we walked homeward - hand in hand; and the light that fell around us seemed to be more pure, more holy, and more divine than it had ever been before.

Chapter 17

One day, as I stood in my lovely room that had become a sacred place for me, I looked into the pictured face of the Christ above me. I felt as though the tender eyes looking down into mine had - in their depths - a pity, a loving compassion that I had never before noticed.

Then, as I began to turn away, I even imagined that His hands reached out from the canvas and rested in benediction upon my head. I stood, for a moment, in blessed peace before Him. As the hands seemed to be withdrawn, I walked over to my sofa to rest.

Strange thoughts and ideas crept into my brain that I had not experienced since my arrival. I felt puzzled and confused. What could it mean? I felt a great heaviness and something similar to *dread* as I tried to lift my head from my pillow, only to fall back again. Surely the old *unrest* of earth could not exist in heaven!

Then, I heard unfamiliar voices. Someone said, "I think her color is better than it has been for several days."

"Yes, there is no doubt that she is better today. I think she might make it! She came very close to leaving this earth."

"Very close to leaving this earth?" As though I had *not* left it - and in returning found my life so altered that gleams of the heavenly realm will fall about my life forever! I have been in my Father's house.

NOTE: *The people mentioned in this book were real, however, their names have been changed.*

Epilogue

In the many letters that were received by the author, after the original publication of this book, repeated inquiries were made regarding whether this was something she actually experienced or was merely a fantasy. Her response to this question was as follows:

"This revelation came to me during a period of great physical suffering and exhaustion. I have always considered it to be sent as compensation for that suffering. At the time, it was as real as any experience in this life could possibly be. Although I can partially forget some of the happiest experiences of my life on earth, time seems only to intensify the wonders of those days when my feet stood upon the border of the two worlds.

"Moment by moment, hour by hour, our souls grew, expanded, and opened to receive fresh drinks of divine instruction, which constantly lifted us nearer to the *Source of all Perfection*.

"It seemed to me that with every step we took in the divine life, our souls reached up toward something better. Like the cup that is overflowing with pure and sparkling water, so our souls were abundantly filled." *

Remarriage is another topic, about which questions were asked time and again. The author admittedly didn't have all of the answers, but expressed these thoughts:

"My *belief* is that as soon as a Christian's soul leaves the earthly body, all jealousy, rivalry, and thoughts that embarrass, grieve, or pain the spirit are gone forever. In heaven there is perpetual love, joy, peace – and happiness without measure. We will feel more "at home" there than we can even imagine on earth. This one thing I know: In heaven there are no conditions that annoy; no questions that exasperate; no ties that conflict.

"It seems to me that it is impossible for two people to occupy the same place in our hearts. Each heart is filled with many compartments, and each beloved guest is assigned his or her own special place, one that belongs exclusively to that individual throughout eternity. No other person can ever occupy another's space. When those we love depart, their special places in our hearts are held in sacred trust for them.

"In heaven, also, no person will ever feel "left out" – the perfect place will be provided for everyone. 'In my Father's house are many mansions. I go to prepare a place for you.' (John 14:2)

"Oh, those wonderful mansions upon which my longing heart looks back! Believe in them - look forward to them - beloved friends, for we have the Savior's promise that they are there. His promises never fail; and I am sure they will not be less beautiful than those I looked upon in my vision.

"So look up, dear friends, and picture your loved ones, as I saw those so dear to me – *happy and blessed beyond all human conception*, in the place of many mansions prepared for us by our loving Father."
*

* Although the sections in quotes have been structurally and artistically altered, the basic content remains the same.

Thoughts to Consider

We have no way of knowing precisely what heaven will be like, but one of my favorite things to do is to try to imagine – in great detail – the most extraordinary heaven God could possibly create, because we do know this:

> "No eye has seen, no ear has heard,
>   and no mind has imagined
> what God has prepared
>   for those who love Him."
> I Corinthians 2:9

Therefore, the reality of heaven will be more wonderful than anything we can imagine – including the vivid images depicted in this book!

As mentioned in the Epilogue, some readers have questioned whether or not the author's experience was anything more than an elaborate dream. It may surprise you to know that the answer is unimportant to me. The value of this narrative, from my perspective, is that it helps us to visualize the reality of heaven, and kindles a passion within our hearts to go there.

This reminds me of a quote by Billy Graham: "Some day you will read or hear that Billy Graham is dead. Don't you believe a word of it. I shall be more alive then than I am now. I will just have changed my address. I will have gone into the presence of God."

Our lives on earth will not last forever. Do you know where YOU will go when your earthly life comes to an end? If your answer is no, please take a few moments to think about the following truths from God's Word – The Bible. (All quotes have been taken from the New Living Translation):

"For all have sinned; all fall short of God's glorious standard."
Romans 3:23

"But if we confess our sins to him, he is faithful and just to forgive us and to cleanse us from every wrong."
I John 1:9

"For God so loved the world that he gave his only Son, so that everyone who believes in him will not perish but have eternal life."
John 3:16

"And this is what God has testified; He has given us eternal life, and this life is in his Son. So whoever has God's Son has life; whoever does not have his Son does not have life. I write this to you who believe in the Son of God, so that you may know you have eternal life."
I John 5:11-13

What a precious gift – to KNOW that we have eternal life! You can have this gift today - this certainty that you will go to heaven when you die, if you sincerely ask Jesus to forgive your sins and come into your heart. *

When you have done this, you can know the scriptures above are your very own – that Jesus died so His children (that includes you!) can live with Him in heaven throughout eternity.

I can hardly wait to go to heaven, be reunited with those I love who have gone before me, and see my Savior's face! I hope, someday, to see yours, too.

Jann Bach

* Although becoming a Christian is so simple that a child can do it, maturing as a Christian is a process that takes a lifetime. True repentance involves trying to live your life in a way that is pleasing to God. I strongly urge you to begin reading from the Bible on a daily basis, starting with the book of John. You can talk to God about absolutely everything (that's prayer)! Ask Him to help you understand the Bible, to guide you with every question, concern, and decision in your life - and to help you find other true believers with whom you can worship.

Helping You Win

Proven Tools to Help in Adjusting to New Life Realities

ASKING TO WIN! (*25th Printing*)
Helping You Win by Asking the Right Profound Questions ...
24 X 7 X 365 X life!

This booklet fits into your suit coat pocket, purse, or briefcase. It contains over 100 profound questions to help you make wise decisions 24 hours a day, 7 days a week, for the rest of your life. Would you benefit from knowing how to ask penetrating, powerful, practical questions? Would you like to be able to ask exactly the "right questions" at the "right time?" This booklet works.

CAREER CHANGE / LIFEWORK
30 Questions to Help You Define Your Next Career Move

Is your current position "just a job," your next "career move," or your "lifework?" This series of 30 questions comes in handy any time you are thinking about the possibility of making a work change. If you are uncertain, these profoundly simple ideas can help. You can also help friends in transition. You hand them the 30 questions; they may take hours to answer the questions, but they will come back with well thought-out answers. These questions save hours of time in decision making. Helpful in any career re-evaluating process between the ages of 25-60. A proven resource!

DREAMING BIG! – Bobb Biehl and Dr. Paul Swets
Your Dreams Are the Key to Energizing Yourself ... and, Your Team

Do you have the NATURAL ENERGY you would like to have on a day-to-day basis? There are many forms of energy ... electrical, caloric, caffeine, social, etc. Natural energy for the human being comes from having a clearly defined *life dream.* **DREAMING BIG!** *takes you step-by-step through a* **31 day process of defining / re-defining** *your life dream. It is also a great tool to help your entire team tap into its NATURAL ENERGY*

ENCOURAGEMENT *In Life's Predictable Valleys –*
(Team Handouts)
A Proven Tool You Can Use to Encourage A
Struggling Team Member

EVERY HUMAN BEING (yes, including me!) "hits a few bumps in the road," has a "blue day" here and there, and occasionally a "bad hair day." In the past 25 years, I have invested approximately 40,000 hours in helping successful executives work their way out of life's predictable valleys and, make progress up life's mountain. These principles have brought perspective and encouragement time and time again. If I were your mentor and you came to me in one of life's predictable valleys, the wisdom found on these sheets is precisely what I would give you. These principles can give you encouraging perspective - any time of the day or night whenever or wherever you (or your team) need it - for the rest of your life. Packet of 20 (11" X 17") copies for team use.

FOCUSING BY ASKING (C.D.) – 20th Printing
Maximize Your Drive Time – by Asking These "Fog Cutting"
Questions – 5 Minutes / Section

Profound questions have helped thousands of people, in all walks of life, at all levels of leadership, focus their lives and teams. This drive-time series is set up with 5-minute tracks, covering the following 10 critical elements of leadership:

Personal Focus –
> Keeping FOCUSED
> Keeping CONFIDENT
> Keeping BALANCED
> Keeping MOTIVATED
> Keeping ORGANIZED

Team Focus –
> Master ASKING
> Master COMMUNICATING
> Master LEADING
> Master MOTIVATING
> Master PLANNING

Whenever you need to see things in crystal-clear focus pop in this drive-time CD.

HEAVEN, My Dream of – Jann Bach
This Inspirational *Book Gives Deep Comfort to a Person*
Anticipating Death or One Grieving the Loss of a Loved One

About 100 years ago Rebecca Ruter Springer had a beautifully vivid dream of what heaven may actually be like. The book has been so helpful that it has been printed many times since then. In this edition Jann Bach has updated the rather stilted original language to make it easy reading for the person suffering from a devastating loss of a loved one. Reading this book helps the grieving person imagine heaven and their loved one being there. It moves the grieving person from,
" _____ is GONE!" to "_____ is NOW IN HEAVEN."

And these few simple words are a major journey in the grieving process. A major tool for anyone whose responsibility it is to help others deal with the grieving process.

MEMORIES – 8th Printing
The Perfect Gift if Your Parents Are Still Living …
Guaranteed to Become a Priceless Family Heirloom Someday!

If your parents, grandparents, favorite aunts and uncles, or mentors are still living this is the perfect gift.

What makes anything literally priceless? Answer: It cannot be replaced regardless of the price you are willing and eager to pay. Once your favorite people on this earth have gone on to their eternal rewards, whatever memories they have written by hand cannot be replaced regardless of the amount of dollars you would be willing to pay. This is one gift absolutely guaranteed to become a priceless family heirloom.

Memories contains over 500 memory-jogging questions to help your loved one relive and write about her or his life's milestones. It's a beautiful album-type book with padded covers and a binding which opens widely for easy writing. Memories is also a "boomerang" gift! You give it to your loved one this year, he or she fills it with memories over the next 1-50 years, then it returns to you as an heirloom for your children's children.

MENTORING - Book *(6ᵗʰ Printing)*
Featured on Focus on the Family
Shows you Step-by-Step How to Become a Mentor or Find One

A mentoring relationship can easily add a feeling of 30-50% extra LEADERSHIP – MANAGEMENT – LIFE horsepower to any person. Without a mentor, a person often feels underpowered, as if not living up to her or his true potential. Ideally...mentoring is a lifelong relationship in which the mentor helps the protégé realize her/his God-given potential. This proven book explains clearly what mentors do and don't do, the nature of the mentor/protégé relationship, the most common roadblocks to effective mentoring, and much more. Mentoring is something anyone can do ... but not everyone should do. A successful mentor doesn't require perfection, and finding a mentor is probably much easier than you think. If you have been praying about a way to have your life make a very, very significant difference ... mentoring may be your life ministry!   Hardback, 215 pages

MIDLIFE MAP
A Healthy Step-by-Step Process Map through the Dangerous Midlife Years
Helps You Realize Your Dreams, Get Your Emotional Needs Met, and AVOID a Midlife Crisis or Drop Out!

This hope-filled book contains a crystal-clear "Midlife Map," which helps guide you or a friend successfully through the very dangerous midlife years. Just because you or your mate is beginning to ask a few midlife questions, does not automatically mean you are experiencing the dreaded "Midlife Crisis." There are three distinctly different midlife phases:

·   Midlife Re-evaluation
·   Midlife Crisis
·   Midlife Drop Out

This book addresses each of the three phases with specific step-by-step instructions on how to avoid the pain and confusion of a midlife crisis…or if you are already there, how to get out and get on with the rest of your life.

WHY YOU DO WHAT YOU DO – 4th Printing
An Extremely Predictable and Easy Way to Understand Yourself and Others without a Shrink

This book is a result of more than 40,000 hours of behind-the-defenses experiences with some of the finest, emotionally healthy leaders of our generation. This model was developed to maximize "healthy" people with a few emotional "mysteries" still unanswered. Why do I have a phobic fear of failure, rejection, or insignificance? Why am I so "driven" to be admired, recognized, appreciated, secure, respected, or accepted? Why am I an enabler, leader, promoter, rescuer, controller, people pleaser? Why am I a perfectionist, workaholic? Why are pastors vulnerable to affairs? Where am I the most vulnerable to temptation? How can I guard against temptation? Why do I have such a hard time relating to my parents when I love them so much? Why do they sometimes seem like such children? These and other "emotional mysteries" can be understood and resolved in the silence of your own heart without years of therapy.

WRITING YOUR FIRST BOOK
Bobb Biehl and Mary Beshear, Ph.D.
This Simple Tool Can Save You Days in Writing Your First Book

If you have been wanting to write a book for years but still haven't produced a manuscript, let Writing Your First Book be your starting point!   Together these two authors have published over 20 books. This is a skeleton outline—no complicated, sophisticated theory or double-talk. It is just a bare bones, easy-to-follow, step-by-step checklist to help you become a royalty-receiving author. A wise investment in your own future.

* Also Available IMMEDIATELY via Download to Your Laptop or IPod

QuickWisdom

<u>Introduction</u>

As an executive mentor / consultant, I have the rare privilege of spending days at a time with some of the finest leaders of our generation. I continue to grow personally, learning more each year than I've learned in the five years before it. Realistically, because of schedule pressures, my personal mentoring is limited to a very few individuals. At the same time, I truly want to see friends like you grow into your God-given potential over your lifetime.

<u>Quick Access to Timeless Wisdom ... 24 X 7 X 365 X Life</u>

Today, every young leader I meet wants wisdom, but needs it fast. We don't have the time with today's pace and pressures to go to a mountaintop and study ancient manuscripts in Sanskrit. Thus ... "Quick Access to Timeless Wisdom." Each month I send 2--3 e-mails ... free of charge ... with the very best "wisdom nuggets" I come across during my consulting to help strengthen you and your friends. I want to keep in touch with friends like you and help you, your family, and your team win!

<u>Your invitation ... Free to you and your friends</u>

QuickWisdom is 100% free to you and your friends. Fortunately, the e-mail technology of today is such that you can enroll 10 friends or 100 to receive the QuickWisdom e-mail. It takes me the same amount of time to send you an e-mail as it does to send it to all of your protegés / friends. I want to use my unique exposure to great wisdom to strengthen you and your friends for a lifetime. Thank you, my friend, for telling your friends about QuickWisdom!

Bobb Biehl
President, Aylen Publishing

To receive these free e-mails simply visit <u>www.QuickWisdom.com</u> and sign up.

PLEASE SEND ME THE FOLLOWING (FREE OF CHARGE):

○ Aylen's Complete – Leadership / Management / Life – Catalogue of Practical Proven Tools

○ Please Sign Me Up for QuickWisdom – FREE

Name_____

Title_____

Organization _____

Address_____

City _____ State _____ Zip _____

Daytime Telephone (   ) _____

Fax (   ) _____

E-Mail   _____

TO REACH AYLEN PUBLISHING BY TELEPHONE, CALL:

Executive Offices — 1 352 735 5252

Fax — 1 352 385 2827

Ordering materials — 1 800 443 1976

Thank You Friend!